CRUZ

Peter Alexander Holman

ISBN-13: 978-0-578-41519-2

The author disclaims responsibility for adverse effects or consequences from the misapplication or injudicious use of the information contained in this book. Mention of resources and associations does not imply an endorsement.

Cover illustration by Bernie Freytag.

Scriptor
PUBLISHING GROUP

TABLE OF CONTENTS

Dedicated to

The Underdog

ABOUT THE AUTHOR

Peter Alexander Holman is a Physical Therapist, certified Strength & Conditioning Specialist, US National Tae Kwon-Do champion and team captain, and two-time Gleason's International Masters boxing champion. His passion for health and fitness has stimulated a successful adjunct career as a product inventor. Producing several products in the fitness industry, most notably the TRX Rip Trainer and the Nautilus Glute Drive, Pete has positively impacted fitness communities on all seven continents.

Pete is a top presenter at IDEA Fit, the largest provider of personal training continuing education in the world, as well as an active contributor to PTontheNet, IDEA Fitness Journal, IronMan Magazine and STACK Magazine. He has appeared on several national TV shows including The Steve Harvey Show and The Doctors, and has trained numerous professional athletes including Hall of Fame football players Jerome

"The BUS" Bettis and Willie "Nasty" Roaf, as well as 8-time X Games gold medalist, Mike Schultz.

Pete's experience competing at the elite level, being coached by transformative mentors and training star athletes has inspired him to write his first book, CRUZ.

"Whether you are an athlete, a coach, a fitness enthusiast or an underdog in life, this book will challenge your thoughts about human potential and instill in you a belief that anything is possible."

Pete can be reached at:

PH1-Performance.com

@PeteHolman1 (Instagram & Twitter)

@PeteHolman (Facebook)

1

NONCONFORMITY

"It is the unknown around the corner that turns my wheels."

—Heinz Stucke,

world record for itinerate bicycle touring in 1995

CRACK, CRACK, CRACK, CRACK—shots echo through the sweltering air that hovers thickly over the desert landscape. I see families running indiscriminately in random directions. A young girl wearing a brown and green flannel shirt and missing a shoe whisked by me with a look of horror on her face. Fleeting amber flashes of machine gun rounds filled the night sky, but it is the smell of gunpowder that stays with me the most; sweet charcoal mixed with sulfur. I can taste it in my mouth. It is thick, lingering, and suffocating. How could something so eviscerating and horrific have led me here? There is something I lost that night that I can never get back. There is also something I gained that I would have never otherwise had. I guess that is the great paradox of life.

Manuel Cruz Delgado gazed thoughtfully out the third story window of his Denver office. The early morning sun gently streamed over the faces of joggers, bikers and commuters as they moved seamlessly back and forth on the meandering path of the South Platte River trail.

"Manuel, your eight o'clock is here," Martha called back on the speaker phone from her reception desk.

"Who is it?" Manuel replied curiously.

"Only the famous reporter, Mark Delatori, who is writing a cover story on you for The New York Times,*" Martha reported with a frustrated sigh.*

"Oh, yes, that's right. Please send him in," Manuel replied.

Mark Delatori walked into the office with a sense of excitement to meet the budding politician. He reached out his hand to greet Manuel and said, "I have heard a lot about you, Mr. Delgado. My editor says that not only will you become the next senator for the great state of Colorado, but you have one of the most fascinating and unbelievable stories she has ever heard."

Manuel took a sip of his coffee, gazed directly into the eyes of the reporter with a look of gratitude and confidence and said, "My story is not dissimilar to that of most Mexican Americans. It is a story of adversity, affliction, and indomitable spirit. However, unlike most Mexicans, my story revolves around a bike."

"A bike?" questioned Mark, obviously surprised by the remark.

A radiant smile spread across Manuel's face as he replied, "Yes, a bike. I'll be happy to tell you all about it, just let me know where you would like me to begin."

Mark Delatori replied, "Where every great story starts . . . from the beginning."

I was born in Tizayuca, Mexico to my mother, Rosina, and my father, José. My dad was a manual laborer who worked tirelessly at a steel factory to provide for our family. A stoic man of few words, Pops was deeply rooted in his Christian faith and made church a mandatory family ritual every Sunday. His faith was evident in his moral standing in the community and in the way he interacted with Mama and me. He often recited passages from the Bible to educate, encourage, or calm us. Even in the worst of times, Pops believed God was watching out for our family.

Pops was also a former professional boxer. He was forced to quit soon after I was born so he could maintain a steady income. Although retired, he still trained every morning at 5:30 a.m. in a makeshift gym connected to the outside of our end-unit apartment. The gym faced east and as the sun crept over the Sierra Gorda mountain range, it would shine on the back of my dad's neck, heating his body and setting his spirit ablaze. In the mornings, I crawled straight out of bed to sit on a flat rock by the gym. I would fold myself into a ball, wipe the sleep from my eyes and sit in silence as I watched Pops "stick and move" effortlessly through the gym.

I was awestruck by Pops. He was only 5'10" but had the physique of a warrior from the Spartan empire. Most of my neighbors were overweight and seemed to lug their bodies around like carcasses eagerly awaiting the morgue. I had only seen super-humans like my father in the *VeloNews* magazines that Pops would bring home from his machine shop. This magazine was the authority on everything and anything having to do with professional road cycling, and it would become a lifeline to me growing up in such a remote village.

"Isn't VeloNews *an American magazine?" inquired Delatori.*

"Yes, it is," Manuel replied.

"How the heck did you get a hold of an obscure American cycling magazine in Tizayuca?" asked Delatori.

"It's actually a funny story about Pops' pompous boss, Rodrigo," Manuel answered.

Rodrigo was a real character and a huge cycling fan. He claimed to be a distant cousin to the famous Spanish 1973 Tour de France winner, Luis Ocaña. Rodrigo bragged obsessively about Ocaña, saying he was the most dominant cyclist the world had ever known and even made up stories trying to excuse Ocaña's rare losses. Rodrigo went as far to claim that the only reason Ocaña didn't win the 1972 Tour de France was because the French team, comprised of stars like Bernard Thévenet, hired an attractive woman to seduce him. According to Rodrigo, the woman was infected with a cold virus and was ordered by the French team to kiss Ocaña. Ocaña subsequently came down with a case of bronchitis which forced him to withdraw in the mountain stages of the 1972 Tour de France. Rodrigo even alleged that Eddy Merckx, arguably the greatest cyclist of all time, was forced into early retirement because of Ocaña's brilliance on a bike. He would constantly annoy my father and the other employees at the shop with preposterous Luis Ocaña sayings that he repeated daily:

"You know, when Ocaña rides a bike, the bike is the one that needs the helmet."

"Ocaña can kill two stones with one bird."

"When there is a solar eclipse, the sun refuses to look Ocaña in the eyes."

"That last one is pretty funny," interjected Delatori. "But I'm confused. What does this have to do with VeloNews*?"*

The only reason my father tolerated Rodrigo's abrasive personality and exaggerated stories about Ocaña was the fact that Rodrigo was a subscriber to *VeloNews*. Rodrigo would give my father his old Velo magazines, which, in turn, he would give to me. We were so poor we really didn't have any reading material in the house. However, because of Rodrigo and *VeloNews*, I could read any time I wanted. *VeloNews* was written in English, but that didn't deter me. I was so fascinated with professional cycling athletes that with my mom's help, I was able to learn English by the time I was ten years old.

VeloNews also had the most exciting stories about American riders, and like every other Mexican kid, I was fascinated with everything having to do with America. I loved learning about the underdog riders from America like Jonathan Boyer and George Mount, and about up and coming phenoms like Greg LeMond. I was moved by the images of Americans riding through the eastern slopes of the Sierra mountain range and dreamt about this mystical, awe-inspiring place in which everyone had fancy cars, multiple pairs of shoes and trained like superheroes.

There was a long pause. Mark Delatori looked down to ensure his recorder was still on, then turned toward the Colorado Senate seat hopeful who was staring out the window. "Sir, are you okay?"

Manuel turned abruptly back towards the reporter. "Yes," he replied. "I just saw someone ride by on a Pinarello. It looked like a Dogma F8. I am sure it had Dura-Ace on it, probably only fifteen pounds." Manuel's office was located next to Confluence Park in Denver where Cherry Creek and the South Platte River meet. The park was an oasis in Denver in which one could kayak rapids, sunbathe on grassy perches or ride bikes along the majestic South Platte.

"Do you want to talk about bikes now?" asked Mark.

"Sorry, I get easily distracted by cycling," Manuel replied with a smile, "I want to tell you more about my father's gym."

Pops' boxing gym was simple and authentic. Underneath a thick plastic awning that covered a ten-foot patch of the outside apartment wall from north to south, was a speed bag, a double end bag and a heavy bag. Weathered and frayed, the Mexican-made Reyes bags still functioned and provided Pops with everything he needed to maintain his timing, rhythm and reflexes. On the wall of the gym were faded and tattered photos of my dad's thirteen professional fights and newspaper clippings of some of his memorable performances. Although my dad had a spotty record of 8-5, he once beat Saul "Superman" Corrales in a headline fight in Mexico City. Saul came into the fight undefeated (18-0) and was talked about as the next Julio César Chávez. My father, a 20-1 underdog, was dropped with an overhand right by Corrales in the first round and relentlessly pummeled into the late rounds. However, in a remarkable and unlikely comeback, Pops delivered his signature left hook to the body in the eleventh round. As Saul took a knee, the fans erupted and famous Mexican boxing announcer, Don "the Juan" Martinez, quipped, "That is quite possibly the hardest body shot I have ever seen. Saul is not getting up from that thunder!" My father's friends who were all in the audience, loved to talk about that fight and nicknamed him "manos de trueno"—hands of thunder.

I cherished the melodic and powerful sound of Pops hitting the speed bag. The repetitive 1-2-3, 1-2-3 became an arioso that crept into my subconscious mind, awakening me slowly and peacefully like a fancy alarm clock. I had read about lavish alarm clocks in *VeloNews*, the kind that can be programmed to awaken you by playing classical music, unlike the traditional clamoring "goose honk" that emanates from cheaper clocks. I was probably the only young boy in the world who didn't need an alarm clock to wake up in the morning. I had my own personal "manos de trueno" ringtone to jostle me out of bed. I remember meticulously studying the old-time photos of my father's matches that were taped to the wall of the training facility. I could recite the newspaper clipping that covered the Corrales fight word for word: "Saul came into the fight hoping for another Superman performance, only to realize some kid from Tizayuca must have packed kryptonite in his gloves." I idolized Pops and would often express my will to follow in his footsteps and become a professional boxer. However, Pops was adamant that it was too dangerous and wanted me to be educated and pursue what he considered a "legitimate" career.

Like most Mexicans living in the villages that surrounded Tizayuca, we were poor. My mom, Rosina, had to work from home to help support the family. My father used to tell me that even right after my birth, Mama juggled breast-feeding, cleaning, cooking, and was still able to continue her work as a subcontractor to a local sweater manufacturer. My mom was not the typical Mexican woman. She didn't care to have multiple children like most Catholic families. When I would beg her for a brother, she would always tell me, "You are all I need, mi pequeño bala de rayos, my little ball of lightning."

She liked to exercise by taking weekend hikes to a cross high atop the Sierra Gorda mountain range. For her, exercise was like a window into the soul. It tested your discipline, gave you courage and provided strength for you in your darkest hour. Mama was bilingual. Her employer worked directly with a distributor in the clothing industry in the United States and told her that if she ever wanted to advance in her career, she would need to learn English. She held me to the same standard. She would say, "Manuel, you are a special boy and one day will do amazing things. However, if you don't learn English, you will not be able to share your gifts with the rest of the world."

My mother was a stunning woman with a curvy figure, plump lips, wavy black hair and wide green eyes which had opened the door to only one heart in her lifetime. She had a small mole on her left cheek, giving her a very distinctive movie star smile which she used abundantly to influence me. She was crazy about Pops and openly flirted with him in front of me.

I would often get annoyed by their open displays of affection and joke, "Go get a room," whenever they got frisky. However, deep inside, I admired my mom's love for Dad and dreamed one day a woman would fawn over me like that. We lived in a 500-square-foot, two-bedroom apartment in a very poor mountainous village on the outskirts of Tizayuca. Although I often dreamed of another physical life, my parents constantly reminded me of the abundant spiritual life we possessed. My parents' largest concern with me approaching my thirteenth birthday was Diablo Negro.

2

EL COHETE ROJO

"As a kid I had a dream—I wanted to own my own bicycle. When I got the bike, I must have been the happiest boy in Liverpool, maybe the world. I lived for that bike. Most kids left their bike in the backyard at night. Not me. I insisted on taking mine indoors and the first night I even kept it in my bed."

—John Lennon,
singer, songwriter, activist and co-founder of the Beatles

Tizayuca wasn't just home to factory workers and seamstresses; it was home to Diablo Negro, one of the largest drug cartels in Mexico. With a soil composition rich in humus and a high percentage of nitrates in the dirt, coca leaves grew with ferocity in the high mountain air surrounding Tizayuca. Protected from rival drug gangs because of the treacherous and exposed roads entering in and out, Diablo Negro had a thriving cocaine distribution business and recruited young boys of the village as runners and henchmen. Diablo Negro was best known for their barbaric treatment of rival gangs and local police. They would often display their power and coerciveness by maiming their rivals and publicly displaying them in the city center. These execution-style gestures had increased in frequency as Diablo Negros' rival gang had grown in numbers and prominence. The power, money and influence of cocaine in Mexico was reaching epidemic heights, and even the Mexican police and military were under huge influence by the drug traffickers. Pops and Mama were terrified of Diablo Negro and extremely concerned the drug gang was going to recruit me into their evil empire. The drug lords would often send young leaders into the villages surrounding Tizayuca looking for adolescents to impress with fancy gifts, usually expensive watches. Once the kids accepted the gifts, they entered into an unwritten contract with Diablo Negro and unknowingly became drug dealers overnight.

Constantly brainstorming on how to shelter and protect me from the ruthless drug lords, one night my father literally fell on the answer. Pops had experienced an exhausting day at work, and while dragging his feet on the way into my room to say hello and catch up on the day's events, he caught his steel-toed boot on the lip of exposed carpet near the entrance of my room. Falling flat on his face, he later recalled to me that he experienced the fall in slow motion. On his descent toward the floor, all he could see was a picture of a beautiful red bike on the cover of a *Velo* magazine I had laying on the floor. Pops realized the solution to Diablo Negro had been staring him in the eyes all this time: a bike.

I remember hollering, "Pops! Pops, are you okay?"

He got up quickly, with a puzzled smile and a trickle of blood running down his nose. He exited my room just as fast as he had entered. Although we were destitute, my parents had desperately wanted to surprise me for my thirteenth birthday with a big present. Mama told me that she and my father had talked about this birthday for several months and couldn't figure out what to do until that fateful night of my father's fall. My dad ran out of my room and into the kitchen where Mama was preparing dinner, with an excitement and passion he rarely possessed at the end of a ten-hour work day.

Let me take a step back—for the most part, my parents were unaware of my obsession with biking. They knew I loved *Velo* magazine, but they believed it was because I got to read about the mystique of America and loved to work on my command over the English language, both of which were true. However, what they didn't know was that I had cut out a page from an old *Ringside* boxing magazine that had been given to Pops by his boss. The article highlighted an up-and-coming

Nicaraguan fighter, Alexis Argüello. Aside from "Manos de Trueno," my favorite fighter was Argüello. I first learned of Argüello when I overheard my father conversing with some other fight fans after church. They talked about a legendary fight in which Argüello moved up in weight to challenge junior lightweight champion, Alfredo Escalera, in Bayamon, Puerto Rico, a fight later named the "Bloody Battle of Bayamon." Escalera had ten straight title defenses and was arguably the best junior lightweight in the world. Escalera was hurt by Argüello early on in the fight but made an amazing comeback in the middle rounds. Both fighters went toe-to-toe and were a bloody mess by the time Argüello finished him off in the thirteenth. Most ring writers call Escalera vs. Argüello "one of the most brutal fights in boxing history."

After hearing about the "Bloody Battle of Bayamon," I fell in love with Argüello's story, his style and his grit. The image I was so infatuated with of Argüello in the *Ringside* magazine didn't show him in the gym hitting a heavy bag, or dancing with the double end bag; it showed him cross-training on a bike. In the image, he was off the saddle, grinding up a Nicaraguan hillside with a drawn, yet determined expression on his face. Even though I read about biking every day in *VeloNews*, when I saw that image, I saw bikes differently. I didn't just see a fighter training in that picture, I saw someone with an unconventional and visionary training approach. I saw an adventurer and free spirit and most importantly, I saw a bridge to simultaneously honor and differentiate myself from my father. For as long as I could remember, I had dreamed of living up to my father's image as a professional boxer. However, on the cusp of my thirteenth birthday, I realized I wanted something different. I didn't know exactly how it would shape me, but that one image of Alexis Argüello biking in the hills of Nicaragua struck such a chord that I was a different person after viewing it. I knew early on that biking would be a transformative part of my life.

"Have you ever felt like that, Mark?" Manuel asked the New York Times *reporter.*

"Let me think about that," Mark said as he reflected for a moment. "When I published my first article for the high school newspaper, I was complimented the next day by a student who asked me some very specific questions about the article. His questions let me know that he had thoroughly read the article and that it resonated deeply with him. For the first time in my life I felt like someone had actually heard me and cared about what I had to say. I guess that's what spurred my career, so, yes, I know how you felt," Delatori replied.

"Exactly. You get it, Mark." Manuel said with enthusiasm. "So, the rest of the story, as later told by my father, goes like this . . . "

Pops went running into the kitchen after plummeting onto his face and whispered in Mama's ear, "I got it."

"Get away from me! You're bleeding," Mama said as she reached for a cloth to help clean up his face.

"I'm being serious, Rosina," said Pops.

"So, what do you have?" asked Mama, dabbing gently around his nose and mouth to clean up the blood.

"Well, Manuel's birthday is in two weeks, and we still don't have a gift for him. Let's get him a bike."

"A bike?" Mama stepped back and looked incredulously at my father. "How are we going to afford a bike?"

"One day, on my way to work, I noticed a red bike at Jesus' garage sale." Pops said.

Jesus ran a local panadería which my father would visit every time he got paid, to stock up on bread.

"I think the bike is still for sale, and maybe Jesus will give us a deal."

"Good luck," Mama said in a sardonic tone. "Despite his first name, Jesus wouldn't give a deal to an orphaned child." she joked.

Undeterred, my father went by Jesus' place the next day after work. Perched against the porch was a red Schwinn Stingray. The bike had a short frame, high-rise handlebars and a long bucket-shaped seat. The design was revolutionary for its time, as it gave kids the ability for fast starts, quick maneuvering and short radius turns. It also looked more like a sports car than a traditional bicycle. My father inspected the machine. It was slightly run-down, but structurally sound.

"My son has a big birthday coming up, and I want to do something special for him. How much for the bike?" Pops asked Jesus.

"El Cohete Rojo? This bike belonged to my son and is a solid machine. I can't take any less than $20," replied Jesus.

Pops paused and offered a sympathetic smile, the kind of smile that acknowledges defeat. With a slumped posture and a gentle sigh, Pops slowly backed away from the bike. As he began to turn his back, Jesus called over to him, "Listen, I have known your boy since his birth, and I have appreciated your business over the years. How 'bout you do some work at my bakery? I have a reserve oven that is down and needs someone with skill to fix it. I will take $15 dollars off the price if you can fix my oven," Jesus said.

"I knew I was right about you. I knew you would pull through for our family. Praise Jesus!" Pops said as he looked up and pointed his finger towards the sky. Then he repeated himself, "Praise Jesus," this time pointing his finger at Jesus. They both laughed, and my father reached out and gave him a big hug.

While in his arms, Pops whispered, "The fruit of the Spirit is love, joy, peace ... Galatians 5:22. You are a good man, and this will not be forgotten."

My father sprinted home with what he was now calling, El Cohete Rojo, "The Red Rocket," in tow. He snuck the bike around back, knowing I would be playing soccer with other boys from the neighborhood in front of the complex. He placed the bike in a community shed behind the apartment complex where he worked on it every night. He took the chain off and soaked it in solvent to clean off the dirt, oil and rust. With a steel brush and file, he cleaned and sharpened the front chainring and rear sprocket. He removed the brakes, seat and handlebar grips, and took the exposed frame to work for sandblasting, to strip off all the existing paint. After buttering-up Rodrigo by telling him that he was presenting a bike to me for my thirteenth birthday in hopes that one day I could ride half as well as Luis Ocaña, Rodrigo allowed him to put the bike frame alongside a batch of floor jacks that were all being powder-coated cherry red. Pops then replaced the handlebar grips with brand new nitro PVC machine grips he found at work, inflated the tires, cleaned the rims, tightened the spokes to true the rims and reinstalled the brakes.

Meanwhile, Mama reupholstered the seat with new, black leather stock she had left over from a side job she had done some time back. She carefully stitched "El Cohete Rojo" in a large gauge red thread on the left side of the seat. After two long weeks of work, my parents had finished their masterpiece. The Red Rocket appeared as if it had just rolled off the assembly line.

I woke up on September 1st to the smell of fresh pozole, my favorite pork and chicken soup recipe which had been passed down from my mother's grandmother. I knew something was up when I didn't hear the repetitive 1-2-3, 1-2-3 rapping of the Reyes speed bag. I jumped out of bed and went to kiss my mom good morning in the kitchen, but no one was there. My excitement grew as I darted out the back door of our apartment. I turned the corner and noticed something peculiar. Pops and Mama were standing next to some sort of object covered by a tarp.

"Papa. Qué es eso?"

"Your mother and I have a special gift for you. Please come forward. Let's all hold hands and pray."

I was so excited, I couldn't bow my head, I just stared at the tarp trying to imagine what was inside.

"Lord, thank you for this most special day of our lives in which thirteen years ago you gave us our only son. You have nurtured us, guided us, watched over us and now you have truly delivered a miracle."

At this moment, Pops slowly pulled the tarp back, unveiling the most amazing bike I had ever seen. Shaking and speechless, I dropped to both knees in front of the bike. I began to sob, not the cool Hollywood sob in which a single tear rolls down the side of a chiseled actor's face, but the uncontrollable sob that involves visceral gurgling sounds, heaving breaths and sporadic convulsions. Not only had I dreamed of owning a bike one day, I was acutely aware of my parents financial struggles and yet, they somehow pulled off this miracle for me. With the tenderness of a doula receiving a newborn child, I gently cradled the handlebar stem with the crux of my right elbow, grasped the seat post with my left hand and embraced the bike like it was the brother I kept asking for and finally received. Mama had her hand on my shoulder, and I looked up to see Pops choking back tears. Mexican men are not supposed to cry. In fact, the only thing that normally leaks out of a boxer's eyes is blood. But on this special day, even "Manos de Trueno," José Alejandro Delgado, shed a tear.

"We have been calling it The Red Rocket, but you can rename it if you like."

"No, Pops. No, Mama. Thank you so, so, so much. El Cohete Rojo, it is. Dios Mio, muchísimas gracias. Yo soy muy contento."

"Sounds like this bike was a big deal," interjected Delatori.

"This bike was more than a big deal. It was my first love," Manuel replied. "Some of my friends were already holding hands and kissing girls behind the school at thirteen years old. However, I developed pretty late in life and wasn't really into girls; but I did understand and recognize true love. From the moment I saw The Red Rocket, I was jettisoned into a love affair with cycling that is still alive today."

Riding became a spiritual act for me, a ritual. The Red Rocket gave me strength, a way to escape my impoverished life and most importantly, a sense of freedom. I embraced that bike like my father had embraced boxing. It wasn't a form of physical exercise, it was an exercise of the heart, born from the spirit that is only known to people who have found true passion in their lives.

I rode daily to school. I rode to visit friends in other villages, and I rode to St. Mary's Church on Wednesday nights to meet my parents for Family Faith. However, my favorite ride took me high atop the Sierra Gorda mountain range, to where an ornate cross that had been built in the early 1900s adorned the mountaintop.

"Wait a minute, is this the same cross your mom would hike to on the weekends?" asked Delatori.

"Exactly! The cross became very special to me for multiple reasons," explained Manuel.

The cross had been constructed by hand in the 1930s by countrymen and was an intrepid symbol for the entire village. Like the first sight of a light tower to a weary sailor, the cross stood as a beacon of hope and a testament to the grit and determination of the inhabitants of the village. The cross also became a psychological asset to me, as I used it as a checkered flag, marking the completion of the brutal ride. I would often meet Mama at the cross on her weekend hikes. We would sit at its base and look down on our village. For a moment we were elevated above the impoverishment that engulfed our village; we stood above the drug violence that plagued Tizayuca and felt like we were resting at the footsteps of heaven.

The route to the cross consisted of twenty-two switchbacks, 1200 feet of elevation and, at points, reached a ridiculous 9% grade, steeper than the notorious L'alpe d'Huez in the French Alps that has tortured many Tour de France riders on their quest for the yellow jersey. The ride was short but brutal, complete with wind exposure, loose dirt, smoldering heat and the infamous final switchback, twenty-two. Switchback twenty-two aimed straight towards the iconic cross atop the mountain and was the longest of the switchbacks. It took me nine months before I could complete this final turn without getting off the Rocket and walking the rest of the way.

The cross was strategically placed on the Sierra Gorda range. Its east-facing exposure highlighted the cross as the sun unveiled itself from the other side of the Earth every morning. I had the entire route memorized in my head—the loose pavement on turns three, nine and ten, the massive cross winds on turn seventeen and the ridiculous 9% grade run-out after turn twenty-two. Not having any knowledge of exercise physiology, I interpreted the burning feeling in my legs, my rapid heart rate, and the raspy cough I got after sprinting the last turn as a religious rite of passage which put me one step closer to God. I imagined that when I died, I would feel the same way I did on turn twenty-two and that the psychological and physical pain would soon be replaced by euphoria, light and peace. The harder I pushed and the more it hurt, the closer I got to God; a theme that seemed to follow me throughout my lifetime. For the next several years, I rode this route four to five times per week without fail. I pushed the envelope on every ride, and every time, The Red Rocket was there to lick the stamps.

3

ONE WAY OUT

"One thing cycling has taught me is that if you can achieve something without a struggle, it's not going to be satisfying."

—Greg LeMond, three-time Tour de France winner

"The suspense is killing me," Delatori said. "How did you find your way to the States?"

Domingo, my uncle, had taken a big risk and illegally crossed the Mexican-American border with his family when I was eight. He found his way to Colorado and was hired on a building crew. The crew ended up being deployed to the mountain town of Aspen to build a lavish house for a United States Congressman on Red Mountain. Domingo was an extremely charismatic man and ended up befriending the estate manager. Eventually, he was offered a position on the grounds crew upon completion of the project.

Domingo and Pops were extremely close growing up in Tizayuca. They used to box in the backyard for hours, hoping that one day they would both be professional fighters and make their way out of the destitute village. However, as they aged, their dreams of boxing fame became obscured by the reality of providing for their families. Although communication between my father and uncle was infrequent, Domingo occasionally wrote on the back of postcards sharing stories about America. He wrote of a life of comfort, a life of beauty and a life without murder and chaos. My family continually talked about America, especially Mama.

As I read about America through the *VeloNews*, my mom learned of the United States through old copies of *People Magazine* rescued from the trash in her supervisor's office. The magazines were filled with ridiculous, scandalous and salacious gossip engulfing Hollywood actors and musicians. However, the pictorial articles also illustrated the physical beauty of America—the pristinely manicured malls in LA, the ostentatiously branded streets of Madison Avenue and the majestic mountains of Aspen.

The beauty, wealth and peace of America contrasted sharply against the recent string of drug violence in Tizayuca. Diablo Negro's leader, El Verdugo, "The Executioner," had been crossed by a man he recently commissioned inside the local police department. The insider was supposed to inform him of any raids on their facilities but failed to do so on a recent sting operation. El Verdugo lost twenty kilos of cocaine, costing him hundreds of thousands of dollars. More upsetting to EI Verdugo than the loss of drugs was the fact that three of his men were killed by gunfire in the raid. He decided that the informant had turned on him and vowed to exact revenge on the entire police force. He instructed his thugs to set fire to a popular strip mall in town. When the first responders and police showed up, they were ambushed by Diablo Negro. The next day, the bodies of four policemen and three firemen were found in the center of town. They had been murdered and had bullseye targets spray-painted on their torsos as they hung from a walkway in the city center. I was seventeen then and had heard and seen countless atrocities carried out by Diablo Negro. I hate to say it, but to some extent I was habituated to the violence.

However, my mother responded much differently. Reading this in the local newspaper, she began to cry. Pops tried to comfort her, but she was inconsolable. In fact, she became uncontrollably agitated. I had never seen her like this. She was visibly upset and began to pace rapidly around the kitchen shrieking, "DIOS MIO, DIOS MIO! They are barbarians! They even killed the firemen. I will not raise a family here! GET US OUT,

José, GET US OUT!" She cried until her voice became raspy, and she collapsed on the floor. My father ordered me to my room. As Pops tried to console Mama, I put my ear up to the door, listening intently.

"It's not that easy, Rosina. Applying for asylum in the United States can take the better part of a year and multiple interviews," I heard Pops whispering.

"I want my family out NOW," Rosina barked back in defiance.

Pops had married my mother shortly after high school. He was her first love, and they had been together for seventeen years. He had never seen her break down like this. It became immediately evident that she was serious. The newspaper article came out on Saturday morning and for the remainder of the day, my parents seemed to hide away and converse. I saw them in the backyard, the bedroom, the kitchen, and at one point, I found them locked in the bathroom engaging in a heated debate. I honestly didn't think much about this strange behavior. Even though I was older and fairly astute, I couldn't fully comprehend what was going on.

After endless talk throughout the day, my father called a family meeting that night. Mama had cooked a beautiful casserole with ground beef, Spanish rice, and pinto beans smothered in cheese. As the family ate, Pops broke the news to me. "Son, as you know, the violence in Tizayuca has us desperately concerned for your safety and for our future here. Aside from the recent atrocities at the strip mall, just last month a boy from your school was killed for refusing to carry drugs for Diablo Negro. We have tried to shelter you from this violence for seventeen years now, but we can no longer protect you. In my last correspondence with your uncle, he informed me that he has work for both your mother and I in America. He even said he could get you into the local high school in Aspen. We know the risk of crossing the border is extreme and this is our home, but we have run out of options."

I tried to be strong, but this was so unfair. How could I be forced to uproot and abandon my life of seventeen years? My eyes began to water. I reminisced about playing soccer in the street with my friends. I thought of Wednesday night Family Faith and visiting my grandparents on the weekend. Most of all, I recognized that my routine of riding to the cross atop the Sierra Gorda range was irreplaceable. With quivering lips, and voice cracking with emotion, I pleaded, "Can I bring The Rocket?"

After a long pause, my father replied, "Yes, son." He forced a smile amidst palpable tension in the room. The gravity of the situation and anxiety of such a large change loomed over us all. Where would we live? How would we get there? What if we got caught? Mama rose from her chair and knelt in front of me, placing her hands on my knees. Pops came from the other side of the table and with one arm around my mother and the other gracing my shoulder, we held one another and wept for what seemed like an eternity.

In one of his latest letters to my father, Uncle Domingo had told him to contact Poncho, the man who successfully helped him cross the border nine years prior. Poncho was a tall, wiry man who had the habit of never looking you in the eyes as he nervously scanned his surrounding environment. Poncho's real name was Javier, but everyone called him Poncho because he had worn the same poncho daily for as long as he lived in our village. He had a sordid past and poor ethical standing, but he was our one way out of the lawlessness plaguing Tizayuca. Since helping Domingo years ago, Poncho had also taken up a new profession; he had become one of Acero's key couriers of cocaine across the border. Acero was a rival drug gang to Diablo Negro and was growing rapidly in numbers. Acero recruited Poncho because of his strong history in human trafficking, which gave him keen insights into the Border Patrol's operations and police activity.

Pops met with Poncho the next week to discuss the details of June 14, 1986, the day that would change our lives forever. Pops reported back and broke down the strategy, "We will all go about business just like it's any other day. In the late afternoon, we will all meet at the house, each pack a small duffle bag of essentials and head out at exactly 7:30 p.m. to meet Poncho at the pick-up location."

He called us over to the living room and pulled up the rug directly under Mama's sewing machine table. "Look, look," he said, prying open a floorboard with a flat head screwdriver. He pulled a paper bag from beneath the floorboard. To our utter amazement, it contained a roll of cash.

"I had no idea," my mom said, as a huge smile spread across her face. She jumped into Pops' arms encircling his waist with her legs and kissed his face. "This was under my feet the whole time?" she asked.

"You were keeping it warm for us," Pops replied.

I couldn't take my eyes off the wad of money. I had never seen more than a few dollars at one time. "How much do you have?" I asked.

"Roughly $300. I have been saving for years for a moment like this. Two hundred dollars is for Poncho, and the rest should cover our expenses for our journey to Aspen," Pops said.

My parents felt guilty for abandoning the country and the people who had supported them for the last thirty-two years. They were proud of their heritage, their culture, and loved, like I did, the mountainous regions of Tizayuca. However, this was an opportunity to escape poverty and crime. Passage to America was a portal to an implausible adventure and a chance to scratch the winning lotto ticket in the game of life. The only thing I insisted on was that I could bring my most prized possession, The Red Rocket. When my father approached Poncho with the request, Poncho thought we were crazy for wanting to bring a bike, but said for an extra $20, he would make it happen.

In retrospect, Poncho was right. We were crazy.

4

VÁMANOS

The most important factor you can control is yourself. I always placed the greatest emphasis on that.”

—Eddy Merckx, five-time Tour de France winner

June 14th came, and like any other day, Pops went to work at the machine shop. Mama put the finishing touches on three beautiful sweaters she'd been knitting for weeks, and I made one final summit to say goodbye to my beacon of hope. At the top of my climb, I got off my bike, knelt at the base of the cross and began to pray. Unlike my father, I wasn't able to eloquently articulate my thoughts about faith. I often stumbled through passages, forgetting key points and placing emphasis on the wrong words. However, on this day my thoughts were clear, my message was concise, and the words seemed to resonate. “Lord, I have never asked for much, and I have praised you for giving me a loving family, a roof over my head and the greatest bike the world has ever seen. But I need you now. Please watch over my family. Keep us safe amidst danger. Instill confidence in us when there is doubt. Shine light where there is darkness and allow your abundant and benevolent love to comfort us through this desperate time." I kissed the base of the cross, arose from my knees and for the last time, began my descent home. The smell of budding milkweed and sweet biznaga wafting up from the earth was a reminder that summer was here. As I glided down the mountainside, the afternoon light occasionally glinted off the cross and flickered onto boulders on the side of the trail serving as a reminder that although I was leaving the cross, the cross was not leaving me.

I entered our house around 4 p.m. Although everyone tried to hide it, the tension was palpable. As instructed, we quickly began to gather our belongings. I placed a comb, deodorant, toothbrush, socks, underwear, three t-shirts and a gray hoodie into my red soccer duffle bag. The gray hoodie, which was two sizes too big, was one my mom had found at a thrift store. It had come all the way from America and said "IMPACT" on the front. This was my "Midas touch" hoodie. In each of my three fastest times up to the cross, I was wearing my IMPACT sweatshirt; it had become my good luck charm.

At 8 p.m., we met Poncho behind the industrial park at the east end of town, not far from where Pops worked. The typically bustling industrial area was unusually quiet. Twenty-two villagers nervously awaiting Poncho's arrival, leaned up against massive concrete slabs of an eerie, vacant loading dock. Soon after, Poncho rolled up in an eighteen-foot truck. The side panels were spray-painted black and the front bumper—dangling precariously from the grill—was secured by an intricate tangle of bungee cords. Mama's breath caught sharply in her chest as she grasped the silver cross that hung from her neck. Her fingers motioned the Holy Trinity. I followed her gaze to three bullet holes in the right rear paneling of the vehicle.

"You okay, Mama?"

"It's nothing, mi hijo. I'm fine. Look, here's Poncho."

Poncho exited the truck in an agitated state. In a curt tone he said, "Everyone pile in the back, quickly and quietly." After seeing my father with The Red Rocket, Poncho began to violently shake his finger from left to right, motioning to him to leave the bike behind. Pops vehemently pleaded with Poncho, but after two minutes of arguing, Poncho raised the bottom of his jacket revealing a Glock 9 handgun.

My father quickly backed down, turned towards Mama and me and said with a stern voice, "Get in the truck." I watched as

Pops gently leaned the bike against a loading dock. Any regret I had of losing my first love that night was instantly eclipsed by feelings of terror regarding our journey.

We were all instructed to climb into 5' x 5' crates used to transport lettuce. "Vámanos! Vámanos!" Poncho yelled out. I panned nervously across the truck to another crate which housed the Diaz family. My brows shot up as I recognized a girl from school, Camila. Her usual light, creamy brown skin was a pale white and her lower lip was trembling so ferociously that it looked like she was shivering. She turned towards me and our eyes briefly locked. I offered her an empathetic smile, but she detected the fear on my face and quickly looked away. Poncho placed the top on the crate, and the Diaz family faded into darkness. That's when I noticed that the lids atop the crates were fake. They were two feet deep and had lettuce heads piled up to the top making the crate appear as if it was full of lettuce. My trust for Poncho and his competency was minimal. Nonetheless, the pseudo lettuce crates were the first slightly impressive thing I had seen him accomplish. With speed, precision and a scowl on his face, Poncho had systematically hidden all twenty-two passengers in the hull of the truck.

Clink, clink, clink, clink, clink ... the back door of the truck slowly descended, and with a shuddering SLAM, extinguished the last sliver of remaining light. Moments later, the engine roared to life and the transmission ground into first gear. The build-up was over. There was no turning back. We were now willing hostages embarking on a journey that would alter the course of our lives forever.

5

DIABLO NEGRO

"You can't win without suffering."

—Bernard Hinault, five-time Tour de France winner

"I can't imagine the fear, uncertainty and vulnerability you must have felt in the back of that truck," said Delatori.

"Yes, had it not been for my father's calm, my faith, and my uncanny ability to fold into a pretzel, I would never have made it," Manuel replied with a smirk on his face. "I have been in many uncomfortable positions in my forty-eight years on this planet, like the time I fell off a balcony and landed upside down in a hibiscus scrub, or the time I ran a marathon for the first time and my calves cramped in the night, pole-vaulting me out of bed every hour ... "

"Ouch!" chimed in Delatori.

Manuel nodded. "But being folded up inside a dark, claustrophobic crate for 11 hours—hands down, the worst!" exclaimed Manuel.

Poncho instructed the twenty-two passengers to be silent during the journey. However, my father couldn't resist offering an occasional prayer. "Do not look forward to what may happen tomorrow. The everlasting Father will either shield you from suffering or he will give you unfailing strength to bear it," Pops said as we rolled out of the industrial park.

I loved my dad's prayers. It wasn't just the meaning and interpretation of the words, it was his soothing voice and authenticity. That was one thing about my father I always admired. He genuinely wanted the best for everyone around him and had no qualms about verbalizing it.

The crate had poor air flow and coupled with the abysmal ventilation in the back of the truck, it was hard to take a full breath. In the desperate silence, I could hear the labored breathing of Mr. Diaz, who was in poor health. There is something about hearing others suffer that churns in your gut. The immediate response is compassion, yet as the hours tick by, it creates anxiety and intensifies your own discomfort. I had to constantly change position to prevent my legs from falling asleep. Between forced breaths and the acute tingling in my legs, I had never been more uncomfortable.

"Are you okay, son?" Pops asked.

"Pops, my legs hurt. I can't breathe. I am so uncomfortable right now," I replied.

"We are close, Manuel. Close your eyes, son. Imagine the beautiful landscape of Colorado; the blue spruce, evergreen and aspen trees gently swaying in the wind. Envision hawks, grouse, and doves floating through the crisp clean air of the Rocky Mountains as deer drink from babbling brooks, and picture ..."

I closed my eyes, and the anxiety and fear I had been feeling since the beginning of the journey was replaced by exhaustion. Listening to my father describe Colorado, I fell into a deep sleep in the darkness of the crate.

The journey from Tizayuca to Laredo, Texas took over eleven hours. We went through towns like Guanajuato, San Luis Potosí, Monterrey and Nuevo León, but I was in darkness for all of them. As I slept, I had a dream about one of the towns we passed through. I saw kids playing soccer in a field of grass as their parents picnicked alongside. Black tar started to ooze out from the earth and the kids' feet became stuck in the tar. Children screamed and cried. As their parents ran to their assistance, they, too, got stuck in the tar. The tar levels rose and rose engulfing the field, the kids and the town.

SMACK! I was abruptly awoken by my head hitting the top of the crate. "That was a big bump. What's going on?" I whispered.

"I think we are close. We are clearly off the main road and traveling over rough terrain. Maybe this is it," replied Pops.

I felt the hair stand up on my arms and any drowsiness left over from my dream state was quickly replaced with nervous excitement. The truck slowed to a stop, and we could hear other vehicles pulling up on all sides of the truck.

"Dad, what's going on? Why are there other vehicles here?" I began to hear passengers whisper concerns from the other crates.

"Be quiet, son. Everything will be okay."

Without warning, the truck switched into reverse and the crates rocked forward as we felt the driver pick up speed. Just as suddenly, we came to another abrupt stop. The crates rocked back the other way, and I reached out my arms to try and steady myself.

"USTEDES! BAJEN!! GET DOWN!" We heard a man yell out in a booming voice.

"Qué pasa, amigo?" Poncho responded.

"BAJEN!" the man repeated.

"La coca? Dónde está ? Where is the cocaine?" the man demanded.

"No lo sé, no lo sé. I don't know," Poncho replied.

Another forceful voice interrupted, this time in English, "OPEN THE TRUCK DOOR!"

"Eso no es necesario," Poncho argued.

BANG!

I had never heard a gunshot before, but this was unmistakable. A thunderous "BOOM" echoed through the back of truck.

"De acuerdo, de acuerdo! Okay, okay!" Poncho responded.

The cargo hull of the truck was silent. My father grabbed Mama and me by the wrists. He squeezed with such force that I felt the lower bones in my wrist shift position. The feeling of uncertainty about what was going to happen swept through the crates like nerve gas. I had experienced this type of feeling only once before. When I was eleven, Mama had a small tumor removed from her chest. Pops and I were in the waiting room of the hospital and as the surgeon came to the waiting room to deliver the biopsy results, the same heavy, ominous and terrifying feeling filled the room.

I realized in that instant that I had no control. I repeated a prayer in my head that my father often said while putting me to bed. "From the unreal lead us to the real, from darkness lead us to light."

Click, click, click, click, click—I could hear the back door of the truck as it rolled up. "Get everyone out of the truck." the man boomed.

Poncho removed the lids from the crates and began extracting passengers. "Esto no es nada. It's no big deal," Poncho tried to reassure us in a shaky voice.

We slowly made our way out of the crates and jumped down from the back of the truck. We could see a crew of seven men fanned out around us.

"Dad, is this Diablo Negro?" I whispered anxiously to my father.

"Shh, son, don't say anything," Pops responded.

They lined us up and told us to place our hands behind our heads with fingers laced together.

"LA COCA? DÓNDE ESTÁ? WHERE IS THE COCAINE?" yelled the man who appeared to be the leader. He wore a black bandana over his mouth and carried a large machine gun strapped over his shoulder as they all did. Diablo

Negro came to life as we felt the ominous presence of this evil group of men.

BANG!

Another shot was fired directly over Poncho's head. We all ducked down and several people shrieked in horror. I could hear a high-pitched ringing in my ears and could feel the energy of the bullet as it whizzed overhead.

"Okay, okay, relax, I will show you where it is," Poncho pleaded.

Poncho jumped up into the truck and opened up a panel behind the crates which was obscured by the view of the gang members. He turned, displaying a block of cocaine with his left hand.

"Mira! Todo está aquí. See? It's all right here," Poncho said as he slowly walked from the back of the truck.

As he held up the cocaine with his left hand, he brought his right hand from behind his belt line revealing an Uzi machine gun. He panned from left to right spraying the gang with bullets. Crack-crack-crack-crack-crack … crack-crack-crack-crack-crack. The crew immediately returned fire, and the night air was ablaze.

The passengers scattered in all directions as the gunmen dropped back. Pops brought me under his right armpit, shielding me from the gunfire. I grabbed my mom by the arm, and we stayed as low as we could, sprinting away from the truck. Pops was holding me so tightly that my feet seemed to float off the ground as we ran.

Just as we made it over a small bluff in the undulating landscape, I felt my right shoulder jolt backwards. I jerked around to see Mama lying in the barren dirt. She had landed in an awkward position with her right leg pinned behind her. I immediately dropped to my knees and tried to scream over the percussive crack, crack, crack of gunfire. I rolled her over onto her back and freed her leg from behind her.

"MAMA, MAMA," I cried out, but there was no response.

The soft winds coming from the east blew her bangs away from her face, revealing her eyes. Her almond-shaped eyes looked upwards, towards the heavens. They were peaceful and steady. Her olive skin glistened. It looked like porcelain as it captured the satiny light of the waning moon.

"POPS, HELP!" I screamed.

But my dad was frozen. With complete chaos swirling around us, my mom lying motionless at my feet, blood oozing from the center of her chest, and the night sky saturated with gunfire, my dad was paralyzed.

"POPS … POPS … POPS" I screamed at the top of my lungs, but he didn't respond.

Looking back towards the truck, the sky looked like a postcard image I had seen of America on the 4th of July. Explosive flashes of light filled the thick night air like fireworks. My dad continued to stand locked in place. The look on his face is something I will never forget. It was the first time I had seen "Manos de Trueno" look so vulnerable and lost.

"POPS, GET DOWN!" I yelled as I let go of Mom and reached up, forcefully tugging on his arm, but it was too late. A bullet entered the side of his head and his body folded to the ground. His eyes were still open as he gazed towards me with a look of disbelief. I looked back towards my mother, whose blouse was now saturated with blood, then back at my father, who was also motionless, eyes still staring at me. I frantically looked from left to right, trying to determine what to do.

The gunfire began to slow, and I noticed members of the gang spreading out to search for survivors. A man ran towards me. I recognized him from the group that met earlier at the Industrial Park. He was young, maybe in his early twenties, and was without family. He came running straight at me and almost tackled me.

"RUN, RUN!" he screamed, looking directly into my face.

He proceeded to grab my arm and physically pulled me off my mom. As I tried to hold onto Mama, my hand dragged across her neckline and ripped the necklace off her chest.

Running in a crouched position towards the north, we noticed someone squeezing through a hole in a chain link fence that spanned across the side of the road. The man pushed me through the hole and we didn't stop running for three hours.

No matter how fast I ran, I could not shake the horrific image of my father, frozen in time, and the fleeting warmth of my mother's hand.

"How could you let this happen?" I looked upward towards God, screaming into the night sky. "How could you let this happen?" I sobbed as I ran.

I was seventeen years old and had lost everything. I would never awake to the melodic pulse of Pops' speed bag. I would never again feel the gentle stroke of my mother's hand through my hair while I fell asleep. I would never ride The Red Rocket high atop the Sierra Gorda mountain range.

I had lost my family. I had lost my home, and on that perilous night, I had even lost my faith.

6

ROCKY MOUNTAIN HIGH

"When the spirits are low, when the day appears dark, when work becomes monotonous, when hope hardly seems worth having, just mount a bicycle and go out for a spin down the road, without thought on anything but the ride you are taking."

—Sir Arthur Conan Doyle,
British writer and creator of Sherlock Holmes

"I am so sorry to hear about your parents, Manuel," Delatori said with deep empathy. "Who was the man that ended up saving your life?"

Manuel moved his head quickly from side to side, shaking back the tears that had surfaced with the memory. He raised his eyes to meet Delatori's gaze and replied, "His name was Juan

Vasquez." There was another moment of silence. Manuel then took a prolonged deep breath and let out a visceral sigh.

The "mystery man" who had helped me escape from the firefight was Juan Vasquez. Juan was a manual laborer whose cousin pleaded with him to come to Phoenix where he worked at a car wash and made excellent tips. Juan told me he was determined to reunite with his cousin and start a new life in America.

"I am so sorry for what happened to your parents. You will get through this, my friend. I promise you," Juan told me.

I didn't have the energy to respond, nor did I have time to process anything that had happened the night before. I just lumbered forward with an expressionless look on my face. We proceeded to walk south towards Laredo in silence.

The mid-morning sun was already scorching our skin and my head was pounding from dehydration. My shriveled stomach began to cramp, folding my body sideways as I walked. Diminished, traumatized and utterly exhausted, we stumbled towards a large truck stop near Highway 359 and Cuatro Vientos Boulevard. The truck stop had just received a product shipment and several large empty boxes had been discarded behind the building. The boxes made for a perfect hiding spot.

"Stay here," Juan said, "I will get us some food and water."

While I hid in a box behind the gas station, Juan went into the truck stop, purchased two large bottles of water and some assorted fruit. He shared the bounty with me and minutes after devouring the food, I passed out. When I awoke, the sun was descending behind a large billboard to the west. I knew I needed to make a move before nightfall.

"Juan," I called out towards the box next to me. There was no reply. "JUAN!" I called out again, a little louder, yet there was still no response. I got up and pivoted the box towards me. Juan was gone. The only thing in the box was a tuna fish sandwich and an envelope. I opened the envelope to find $100 U.S. and a note which read, "Vaya con Dios, mi amigo."

I wolfed down the tuna fish sandwich, folded up the $100 bill and put it in my sock, and then crumpled up the note and threw it away. I was alone now ... completely alone.

The English lessons Mama had given me and the late-night reading of *VeloNews* proved invaluable as I tried to navigate southern Texas. I took some deep breaths, clenched my fists and made my way to the front of the gas station. I politely asked a gas station employee, "Do you know where the closest bus station is?"

The attendant replied in a curt voice "Why? You headin' back to Tijuana, where you belong?" I knew I was going to experience racism in America, I just didn't realize it was going to happen so quickly. Were the positive descriptions my parents gave of America being the land of opportunity and the melting pot of the world just fallacies?

I rushed out of the truck stop stricken with loneliness, dejection and fear. For as long as I could remember, I had learned of God's omnipotence and omniscience. Stories told in church about God protecting and nurturing his children—were these all illusions? "How can God be so cruel?" I asked myself. First, he allows my parents to be violently taken from me and now he strips me of my dignity. Clutching my mother's silver cross necklace, I cocked my arm back and hurled it into a shrub brush at the edge of the parking lot.

Turning back towards the gas pumps, I saw two young men jump into their Westfalia camper. As the driver started the engine, he looked directly into my eyes. He must have noticed my despondent look. Sticking his head out the window he asked, "Hey, buddy, you need a ride? I am dropping my friend off at the bus station and can give you a lift."

Without any options, I quickly agreed and jumped in the back. As the camper pulled out of the station I yelled, "WAIT!" The driver pulled over and I jumped out of the camper, ran over to where I had thrown the necklace in the brush and retrieved my mother's cross which was hanging perfectly from one of the scraggly branches.

There were two young men in the camper. They were in their early twenties. Both had shoulder-length hair and smelled of incense. "Hey, bro, where you heading?" the driver asked.

"I am going to the mountains of Colorado where my uncle lives," I responded.

"Solid! We just toured through there and did some epic rock climbing, kayaking and camping. You're going to love the Rocky Mountain way, dude." On cue, the driver's friend put a tape into the cassette deck. The music to "Rocky Mountain Way," a compilation album by Joe Walsh, started to play and became my first introduction to American rock 'n roll. I immediately loved it.

The driver asked, "Where you from, brother?"

I was too scared to say anything about my origins, so I diverted the conversation. "Why do you call me brother?" I asked.

"We're all brothers and sisters, man. I'm brother Steve, this is brother Mark and you're brother …? What's your name, brother?"

I hesitated for a second before I replied, "Brother Manuel."

They both laughed. "You see? We all come from the same place. We might look different, talk different, smoke different weed, but we're all brothers and sisters, man, just little drops of water from the same massive ocean."

The simplicity and reverence of what this guy said instantly comforted me and erased the hateful language used by the truck stop employee. These guys had a sense of freedom that was foreign to a small-town boy from Tizayuca.

"What do you guys do?" I asked.

"We live," replied Steve. "Well, let me rephrase that. We worked our butts off for two years after getting out of college, and then decided to take some time off to explore the world and get to know ourselves."

"Get to know yourselves? Don't you know who you are?" I replied skeptically.

"I am still learning who I am, my friend; still learning what excites me, what I am passionate about and what I can turn into a career," answered Steve. "If you're so sure of yourself, then who are you?" asked Steve.

I had never been asked this question. I paused for what seemed to be an eternity, then replied, "I am the son of José and Rosina Delgado."

Steve looked back at me and nodded. "Right on, man."

Soon after, the car pulled into a parking lot. "Well, this is the bus stop, brother. I wish you a safe, peaceful, and epic journey," Steve said as he held out his hand in what I would come to know as the "bro-shake." As the two young men drove away from the bus stop, Steve stuck his head out the window and said, "You will always be a son, Manuel, but one day you will be much more."

7

DELIVERANCE

"Life is like riding a bicycle. To keep your balance, you must keep moving."

—Albert Einstein, German-born physicist who discovered the Theory of Relativity

I approached the ticketing window at the bus station and asked a very peculiar-looking man for a one-way ticket to Aspen. I had never seen a handlebar mustache before and this thing was a beauty—wide, thick and prominent. "Ain't no such thing as a one-way to Aspen. Closest I can get you is Glenwood Springs."

"I'll take it," I quickly responded. I handed over the $100 bill and "cowboy" gave me back $24 in change. That didn't leave me with much, but I was on my way.

I arrived in Glenwood Springs the next morning, physically and mentally exhausted. Every time I drifted off to sleep on the bus, I had the same nightmare. There I sat, Indian-style, in a field of sparse sagebrush and broken rock, cradling my mother's head in my hands as blood trickled from her sternum. Lying still next to us, my father looked upwards into the night sky as if he was looking past the stars, past the Milky Way and into another dimension. The velvety Chinook winds gently blew my mother's bangs across her face, exposing her forehead. It was the same forehead that had nuzzled up to my chest when I was down, the same forehead that furled upward in excitement when I brought home straight A's, and the same forehead that would rest against my father's during an intimate moment at the end of a long day. It was the look on my mother's face that haunted me. She looked so peaceful, so content. She just kept smiling and looking up at me with radiant green angel eyes.

Then I would awaken. The panic of what lay ahead was toxic. My heart raced, my palms began to sweat, and my stomach cramped. Sometimes I would look out towards the back of the bus calling out in my head, "Mama? Pops?" in hopes that somehow they would magically appear.

My first step off the bus in Glenwood Springs nearly twenty hours later was met with a familiar feeling. Even though the town of Tizayuca was severely impoverished, its mountains were pristine. Filled with high alpine trees, brightly-colored wildflowers and purified air, Tizayuca's topography was something of a marvel. The landscape of Glenwood was not dissimilar. I took a deep breath to test the air. I could smell the resin that drifted off the aspen trees, the mint and piñon coming from the dry sage, and the sweet aroma wafting off the red rock formations. After a brief peaceful moment, I became laser-focused on a plan to find Uncle Domingo.

I remembered watching in amazement as my father would hit the speed bag. The speed bag has been a boxing staple going back to the all-time greats like Rocky Marciano and Jack Dempsey. These iconic fighters used the speed bag to train for endurance, timing, rhythm and efficiency; but most importantly, they used it for focus. I used to interrogate Pops with questions while he hit the bag. "Why does the sun rise in the east and set in the west? How come I don't have a brother? How did you know mama was the one? In between the percussive 1-2-3 … 1-2-3 … 1-2-3 of the bag, my dad would answer without missing a beat. "The sun sets in the West because the earth spins towards the East; you don't have a brother because you are all we need, and when you find the right woman, you just know it." Like crosshairs locked in on target, his focus was undeterred, unwavering and impenetrable. This was the type of focus I would need right now if I was going to find my uncle. I had no physical address, no map, and was traveling to a town I had yet to see. All I could remember about Uncle Domingo was that he still practiced boxing and possibly martial arts. If I could find the gym he trained at, maybe I could find him.

I noticed an International House of Pancakes restaurant directly across from where the bus dropped me off. I entered the restaurant and a heavyset woman with a jovial smile greeted me: "What ya' need, honey?" she asked.

"What is the cheapest way to get to Aspen?" I replied.

"You see that large awning across the street with the blue sign that says RFTA?" I nodded. "That is the local bus that can take you to the BIG TIME."

"Big time?" I replied inquisitively.

"Yeah, you said you were going to Aspen, right?" I nodded. "Well, then, enjoy the BIG TIME!" she repeated.

On my way to the bus stop I passed an Army Surplus store which had a sale rack of clothes outside its door. I checked my pocket to find only a few dollars of cash and started to turn away. Pausing to smell my armpits, I quickly turned back and began to comb through the rack. I found a white Champion t-shirt and took it inside to buy.

"Do you have a restroom I can use, sir?" Although I was still learning proper English, I had nailed this phrase.

"Around the back," the man replied.

I entered the bathroom and for the first time since I had departed from Tizayuca, saw myself in the mirror. I was a wreck. There was blood smeared on my shirt, my face was gritty and covered with dirt and my hair was completely matted down on the right side of my head from sleeping on the bus. I spent several minutes washing my face, armpits and chest with soapy water. I wet my hair and brushed through it with my fingers until the wave came back, and put on the new, crisp, white shirt I had purchased. It wasn't perfect, but I exited the bathroom feeling somewhat "put together."

I made my way onto a RFTA bus that would travel through Carbondale, El Jebel, Basalt and Snowmass, en route to Aspen. I noticed many Hispanic individuals getting on and off the bus and overheard a group of younger guys talking in Spanish about girls, parties and work. "Qué pasa, amigo?" I asked one of the boys. "Do you know where there is a martial arts studio in Aspen?"

"Why, are you the Karate Kid?" the boy replied, as his group chuckled.

"No," I said smiling, "just trying to find a friend."

"Hold on," the boy said. He worked his way up towards the front of the bus and engaged a large male. I was impressed with this man's presence as I had watched him enter the bus after me. He wore a Bulova watch, a gold chain around his neck and dark sunglasses that I had only seen fancy Hollywood actors wear in *People Magazine*. The boy came back and assumed the crane stance.

"Crane stance? What the heck is that?" Delatori interrupted.

"You don't remember the epic scene from The Karate Kid *in which Daniel-san is about to defeat the Cobra Kai student while balancing on one leg?" Manuel asked as he rose up from his chair. He unbuttoned his blazer, stood on one leg with his other leg flexed to 90 degrees and stretched his arms out like a crane.*

"Oh yeah! That scene was amazing! So, was the kid joking?" Delatori responded.

"Yes, he was," Manuel replied, "and although I had yet to see the movie, I understood the joke."

The "Karate Kid's" entourage began to chuckle, and I joined in. "The only two martial arts places are the karate studio in the Airport Business Center (ABC) and some Aikido dude that practices out of the Aspen Meadows," the "Karate Kid" informed me.

"Muchisimas gracias," I replied.

I first tried the karate studio located at the ABC Industrial Park, ten minutes west of Aspen. After wandering aimlessly around the large industrial park, I turned a corner past the Louis Swiss Bakery and saw a Japanese flag hanging from the side of a two-story building. Entering the structure, I quickly realized I had found it. A class was just starting to line up and a petite woman, adorned with a crisp white uniform, four yellow patches stacked on her left shoulder and a black belt cinched around her waist, appeared. "Can I help you?" she asked with a thick Japanese accent.

"I am looking for Domingo Delgado. Does he train here?"

"Ha, ha, ha," the instructor replied. "No, he used to train here, but we had to let him go. You can probably find him either at the Aspen Meadows Aikido—They take anybody there—" she quipped. "Or he might be at the Green Turtle Liquors," she said, laughing once again. The woman spoke fast, and I struggled to understand her English. Some of the other students were chuckling, so I smiled along. I did understand her comment about Aikido at the Aspen Meadows, though, and proceeded to thank her in a soft voice before I quickly left the dojo. As I walked by the automotive shop next door, I saw a mechanic outside and asked him where I could find the Aspen Meadows. He gave me instructions, and I proceeded east on foot.

The twenty-minute walk east of the ABC was one of the most beautiful walks I had ever taken. After exiting the crowded industrial complex across from the Aspen Airport, a trail opened up that led along the Aspen Municipal Golf Course. The radiant green grass on the tee boxes and putting greens was perfectly manicured and looked like it had been cut by hand. The trail then meandered through a meadow of open space where a lush community garden overflowed with ripe tomatoes, sunflowers and lettuce. Finally, after following the bike path across Cemetery Lane and crossing the bridge on the north walkway, I turned left and the trail led me into a thickly populated grove of aspen trees where the Aspen Meadows resort was located.

I found my way to the health club and was directed to the Aikido dojo towards the west side of the facility. The doors to the dojo were closed, but through the frosted glass I could see a number of students kneeling down. It was quiet. There was no labored breathing, no sounds of speed bags like I had grown up with. No one was talking. It was silent.

Suddenly, a strong voice bellowed, "OSS." Immediately, students rose to their feet, and the door slowly opened.

I was extremely nervous. Even if I was lucky enough to see my uncle, would we recognize one another after all these years? I entered the dojo and noticed a middle-aged man in the corner of the room with his back facing the door. The man had taken off his gi, the orthodox training top worn by Japanese martial arts practitioners. I marveled at the man's silhouette which highlighted a v-shaped back, mapping out a life of hard work and athletic endeavor. The man wore his hair in a ponytail, and upon doffing the elastic tie, a beautiful mane of thick brown hair appeared. Could this be Domingo? I felt a heaviness in my chest, and my face flushed. The man turned toward the front door. His piercing green eyes locked onto mine. Then his eyebrows scrunched inward, creating a puzzled expression on his face.

Over the last several days, I had been as stoic and brave as possible. However, in that moment, something shifted, and I began to tremble. In a quivering voice, I whispered, "Domingo?"

"MANUEL CRUZ DELGADO," the man replied as he opened his arms, lunged forward and swept me up into a strong embrace. We hugged briefly, and then I collapsed, falling to my knees on the floor. My hands covered my face as I began to sob. The last time I had seen Domingo was at Christmas when I was eight years old. He had given me a pair of silver, special edition, Cleto Reyes boxing gloves. I never will forget the smell of the fresh leather and shiny appearance of those gloves. They looked like the glitter that adorns the star atop a fancy Christmas tree. Domingo grabbed my face with his hands and said, "Mi hijo, qué es esto? Qué es esto? My son, what is it, what is it?"

"They're dead, Domi," I cried, using the nickname I had given my uncle years ago. They're both dead!"

"Who's dead, Manny?" asked Domingo.

"My parents," I replied, once again breaking down in tears and crumbling into his arms. At this point we had the attention of the remaining students, and even the instructor. Domi gathered me up and helped me to the warming room. He made me chamomile tea with lemon and honey and we sat down on a soft couch next to a fireplace.

"Tell me, son, what happened? I must know." Two hours passed as Domingo learned how his brother and sister-in-law were brutally gunned down, how I escaped with the aid of Juan Vasquez and how I found my way to Aspen. Domingo, also in tears by this time, informed me that he, too, had lost his family. Although sober now, he was an alcoholic, and as a result of his terrible behavior, his wife and two kids had moved to Arizona. He told me that the move from Tizayuca had been very hard on them and that he got into a bad element early on in Aspen. As he came to the end of his story, Domingo said, "But I am clean now, Manuel, and there is a reason you have made it all the way here. You are now my son, and I will take care of you. I will never let anything happen to you." Domingo said. Although I hadn't been terribly close with Domi, this single conversation bridged a nine-year gap, and solidified the love and strength born out of the Delgado family. "Manny, let's go.

You need food, a warm bath and a good night's sleep, mi hijo."
I had no words, just a sad smile and a cascade of tears. Domingo escorted me out of the warming room. He draped his arm around my shoulders, and as we walked out of the Meadows, our heads gently leaned against one another. I was home.

8

HOME

"Good is something you do,
not something you talk about. Some medals
are pinned to your soul, not to your jacket."

—Gino Bartali, winner of the 1938 Tour de France and two-time winner of the Giro d'Italia

We pulled into a long driveway. The berms on either side displayed an array of brightly-colored wildflowers blending into small groves of aspen trees, and the entrance was marked by a large bronze grizzly bear statue standing on its hind legs. Aspen trees are not native to Tizayuca and were foreign to me. The aspen leaves seemed to dance in the wind and as I opened the passenger window, I imagined they were clapping for me as I had finally made it home. Domi drove the truck around to the back of the estate, which looked more like a compound than a residence.

The house was massive, 15,000 square feet, with beautiful architecture featuring oak beams and stone siding. Despite its massive scale, the house appeared to blend into the surrounding environment and provided a sense of calm. "We're home," Domi said.

We rounded a corner and traveled down a short dirt road to an earthy cabin in the back of the estate. The cabin was made of sturdy logs held together by thick chinking which covered up the imperfect joints. Even from the outside, it looked warm and inviting. Behind the cabin I could see the Roaring Fork River to the south. Domi escorted me inside and led me down a short hallway to my room. He opened the door to my new room. It had a pinewood bed and matching desk. A large TV sat on a shelf against the wall, and through a sliding glass door, I could access the back porch, which looked out towards the river. The most intriguing part of the room was the comforter. It was five inches thick with an ornate image of a bear family walking through a forest of aspen trees. Colors of red, brown and green bounced off the surface. Its richness made it look like a piece that should hang from a wall in an art museum, not adorn my bed. I dove towards the bed and with the form of a gymnast, rotated in mid-air to land face up with legs and arms crossed. Watching me with adoration, Domi smiled as he sat down at the edge of the bed.

"I remember when your dad and I would wrestle, tell stories and joke with each other before we went to bed," he said. I could see the flood of memories washing across his face as he continued. "Your dad and I used to box together, too. I showed him footwork drills, how to use the speed bag and how to "dig to the body" with his left hook."

"MANOS DE TRUENO," we both said in unison and smiled at each other.

"He was a hard worker, Manny, and he practiced everything I showed him, over and over, until he felt like he had mastered it. He always looked up to me ..." Domi's voice trailed off, his eyes lowered, and a sad smile settled on his lips.

"You want to know the fondest memory I have of your father?" Domi asked, as his eyes drifted up towards mine.

"Yes, Domi, I want to know." I exclaimed.

"I will always remember the look on my brother's face the day you were born. Of all the things he accomplished in his life, the thing he was most proud of, was being your father."

Tears rimmed Domi's eyes. He sniffed and slowly shook his head in disbelief. "Get some sleep, Manuel. Tomorrow is a big day. We need to get you registered for summer school."

"SCHOOL? I don't think I am ready, Domi," I responded in a panicked tone.

"Manuel, you are my responsibility now. You are all I have, and I am not going to let you fall behind. You need to work on your English and get familiar with where you will be attending school this fall. I will have breakfast ready at 7 a.m., maybe even have some chile rellenos for your first day. Sleep well, my son." Domi gently brushed the hair back on my head, leaned over, kissed me on the forehead and whispered, "Te amo, mi hijo. I love you, my son."

Domi turned the lights off as he left the room. A sliver of moonlight beamed in from the porch door, illuminating a desk lamp made of deer antlers. I had never seen a lamp made of antlers. It was ornate and exquisitely beautiful but seemed to be missing something. I jumped up out of bed and rummaged through my jeans. Where is it? A sense of panic rushed through my body. Where is it? I dug into the rear pockets. Nothing! I dug into the right front pocket and still nothing! I dug deep into the left front pocket of my jeans and finally felt it. I let out my breath in a sigh of relief.

Pops bought Mama the sterling silver necklace after receiving a small purse from his win against Saul Corrales in Mexico City. He told me that the morning after the fight, he got down on his knee while they were out to breakfast and presented her a small velvet box. He looked up at her with his left eye completely swollen shut and lip split open. "You promise that you will be with me until the end, Rosina?" he asked as he opened the box revealing a timeless sterling necklace with silver cross pendant.

"I will be with you for all eternity, my love," she replied as Pops took the necklace out of the box and delicately placed it around her neck. After that, the pendant never left her neck until the dreadful night I seized it from her lifeless body at the border.

I slowly pulled the necklace from my jeans and hung it on one of the antlers of the desk lamp before laying back down on the bed. As the cross pendant captured the glittering moon rays streaming in through the curtain, I thought about Mama, remembering her warm smile, comforting embrace and almond-shaped eyes. I thought of how she used to read to me and gently stroke my hair as I fell asleep at night. I closed my eyes, and as I drifted off, I thought I could even smell her perfume.

9

FINDING YOUR GROOVE

"Sometimes, when we train, we simply have to go out to meet the Man with the Hammer."

—LAURENT FIGNON, TWO TIME WINNER OF THE TOUR DE FRANCE AND ONE-TIME WINNER OF THE GIRO D'ITALIA

Delatori's voice pulled Manuel back to the present. "Did you seriously make it to summer school the next day after all you had been through?"

"Well, it was close." Manuel replied. "Domi had lived through some big-time failures in his life and when I showed up on his doorstep, it was his chance for redemption. In Domingo's eyes, if I didn't get started with summer school and meet the teachers, befriend some students and try to assimilate into the program, it would be much harder as time passed."

"I guess it makes sense in theory," Delatori nodded in understanding, "but jeez."

"Whether it made sense or not, there I was."

I awoke at 6 a.m., staggered to my feet and looked around the room. My new surroundings were disorienting. I kept blinking my eyes in hopes that I would open them to the comfort and familiarity of my room in Tizayuca and soon be greeted by Mama and Pops. Domi had left some Levi's jeans, a fresh white t-shirt and a pair of blue-and-white-checkered Vans on the desk. Looking back at my attire, I must have looked like the Mexican version of Spicoli from the movie, *Fast Times at Ridgemont High*. I was led to the kitchen by the seductive smell of chili rellenos. "Wakey, wakey," said Domingo as I entered. "This is the first day of your new life in Aspen, son. How do you feel?"

I was not excited about school. I was tired, and still deeply mourning my parents. I was also nervous about fitting into a new school with predominantly wealthy white kids. "Not so great, Domi," I said in a downtrodden voice.

"Listen, son, you have your father's good looks, your mother's charm and my big huevos! Most importantly, you are a

Delgado, and we are fighters. You are going to do special things at Aspen High School. Something I learned in Aikido is that whenever you feel your emotions taking over, focus on your breath and think about one image that brings you comfort," Domi said. "What image brings you comfort, son?"

"I am not sure, Domi."

"Think, son. When is it that you feel at peace? When is it that you are in the moment and happy to be alive?" Suddenly, I remembered the soft winds blowing off the top of the Sierra Gorda mountain range, the radiant glow of the late day sun and the feeling of comfort and accomplishment I had standing at the summit of what felt like the top of the world.

"Manny? Manny? Lost you there for a second," Domi said, snapping me out of my reverie. "Vámanos, mi hijo." We jumped into Domi's Jeep Wagoneer and were greeted by unique Latin guitar sounds on the stereo.

"Who is this?" I asked inquisitively.

"Only the greatest Mexican musician to ever pick up a guitar: Carlos Santana."

Music was blaring out of the speakers; I began to smile at Domi's enthusiasm as he yelled "CARLOOOOOOSSSSSS" and we took off towards school.

As we pulled up to the school, Domingo noticed a friend of his who worked on the maintenance staff and immediately yelled out, "Qué pasa, amigo? Este es mi sobrino, Manuel."

I was horrified, "Domi, if I am going to fit in, I need to be more vanilla and less vato."

"Listen, Manuel, your grandparents are Mexican, your parents are Mexican and you, my friend, are Mexican. You can fit in, but always embrace your heritage. It makes you, you."

Domingo walked me into the Administration Office, where I waited for about a half hour while he spoke with the vice principal. When they came out of the office, Vice Principal Sanders said, "Welcome to Aspen High School." As he shook my hand, he continued, "This is pretty unusual, but considering the circumstances, we are going to do everything in our power to get you started today. I will have my assistant escort you to class and help make you feel comfortable in your new school."

"Thanks, I appreciate it," I replied. Domi gave me a big hug, and as he walked away, raised his right fist in the air as if to say, "You've got this!"

The assistant led me down the hall towards the east side of the building. "Wait here for a moment," she said as she popped into a classroom along the way. I stood at the doorway and peered inside. There were several younger kids inside the room;

one boy was rocking back in forth in his chair, another girl seemed to be visibly upset, and another child sat with his back towards the front of the class. The assistant began to talk to a young woman in the front of the room. I couldn't help but notice the presence of the young woman; I stood catatonic, transfixed by her beauty. The girl must have sensed me staring at her and glanced over towards me, I quickly ducked out of the doorway, embarrassed to be caught staring.

"What class is that?" I politely asked the assistant upon her return.

"During the summer months the high school hosts a class for developmentally disabled kids called *Finding your Groove*. It is a great opportunity for high school students to volunteer and get experience as they help teach the class. "Follow me, we are almost there."

In a moment, we entered another classroom and to my surprise, it was filled with kids who looked just like me.

"Manuel, please meet Mr. Garcia, he runs our language assimilation program."

A small man with an infectious smile reached out his hand; "Welcome to Aspen, my friend," he said. Please take a seat. Mr. Garcia began to address the class in Spanish. "Welcome to language assimilation: quite possibly the most important class you will ever take in your lifetime. Each and every one of you is a uniquely intelligent and beautiful human being, however, if your English isn't fluent, no one outside of your friends and family is going to know. Thus, this will be the last time I address you in your native tongue." One of the boys sitting to my right looked at me in disbelief. I looked back at him with a curious smile as my nervousness and anxiety melted away. I had dreamt of learning English throughout my whole life, and this seemed like a golden opportunity.

The summer flew by. I studied English every day and every night and had many conversations with Uncle Domi, whose English was superb. I also made it a special point to periodically walk by the *Finding your Groove* class to catch a glimpse of the stunning mystery girl. Occasionally our eyes would meet, and it became increasingly difficult to pretend I wasn't noticing her. On the weekends, I helped Domi with landscaping, pruning trees and even learned how to operate a small tractor. In the evenings, Domi and I would often sit on his back porch looking out at the river. I would beg him to tell me stories about my dad, his childhood and his boxing exploits—of course, all in English. We laughed and cried and many times, I found myself gazing up towards the infinite stars high above the Rocky Mountains wondering if my parents were looking back down at me. Every night I laid in bed gazing at Mama's necklace as I tried to fall asleep. I often thought about my faith and would try to bargain with God; if he would return my parents, I would never question his love and would start going to church again. Yet, every morning I awoke, feeling alone, empty and faithless.

10

MOUNTAIN BARBIE

"Winning is about heart, not just legs, it's got to be in the right place."

—Lance Armstrong, cancer survivor and former professional road racing cyclist

"Are you ready for this?" Domi said as I tried to finish the full plate of huevos rancheros he had lovingly made for me. Usually I scarfed down breakfast, but on this day my stomach was so upset I had to force myself to eat.

"No," I replied nervously.

The first day of high school for seniors should be brimming with bravado, confidence and even a little bit of swagger. However, I was still trying to make sense of losing my parents and not having made any real friends at summer school, felt completely alone. Uncertainty and anxiety filled the room and took up residence in the pit of my stomach.

"Do you remember your father telling you about his fight with Corrales? He was getting pummeled. His eye was swollen shut and he was physically exhausted, and then what did he do in the 11th?"

I broke into a smile as we both said in unison, "Manos de Trueno," which had become our new catch phrase.

"You got this son," Domi said as he pointed towards me.

We pulled up towards the front of the school in Domi's Jeep. He put his right hand behind my neck and gently pulled me toward him until our foreheads met.

"Son, it is up to you to carry the greatness that your parents worked so hard to create into the next generation. Your English has really improved, and I believe in my heart you are ready for this." He kissed me on the forehead and as I grabbed my backpack and slung it over my shoulder, he yelled out of the car window, "Stay present. This is your time."

I had never seen more white people in polo shirts and clean shoes in my entire life. The new desks, unblemished floors, and inspirational posters adorning the homeroom made it look more like City Hall in Tizayuca than a high school classroom. I took a seat near the middle of the class as kids began to filter in.

"Hey, homie, that's my seat," said a tall kid with long, flowing blonde hair. I later learned that his name was Johnny Roberts. He was the son of Mike Roberts, one of the largest commercial real estate developers in the United States. Johnny was captain of the high school cycling and ski teams.

"Sorry about that," I said as I got up out of his seat and moved towards the back. "Off to a great start," I thought to myself in a sarcastic tone. I found a seat three rows back and apprehensively settled in.

As the classroom started to fill up, I nervously kept my head down trying to avoid eye contact with anyone. A pair of pink converse high top shoes with bright white laces caught my eye as they walked towards me. I glanced up and to my surprise, there she was, the mystery girl. Her wavy blonde hair bobbed over her shoulders as she floated towards the back of the room. She wore a knee-length floral-patterned sundress that gently hugged her body, showing off her curvy but athletic frame. My eyes magnetically drifted upward as she came down the aisle. With a tall posture and confident gait, she proceeded to sit down right next to me. I tried not to stare, but we quickly caught eyes.

"Hi, I'm Summer. Aren't you the kid from summer school?"

I tried to answer, but I was hypnotized by her eyes. They were the same color as the turquoise waters off the southwestern coast of Mexico. I was frozen, speechless, intoxicated.

Just then the bell rang, and Mr. Hightower, who had been busy organizing his desk and looking somewhat frazzled on the first day, began to address the class. "I want to welcome a new student; his name is Manuel Delgado."

Just then, oblivious to Mr. Hightower's introduction, I gathered my nerve, leaned over to Summer and said, "My name is Manuel."

Summer smiled and said, "Yeah, that's what Mr. Hightower just said."

"Off to an even a greater start," I thought to myself again, shaking my head in disbelief.

I survived my first-period embarrassment with "Mountain Barbie" and then attended math class, social studies, and finally, science. Although I was struggling to stay focused in the other classes, I was intrigued by science. The class lesson that day touched on cellular biology and the sympathetic nervous system. I was fascinated and excited to learn more about the human body. We were introduced to cells and cellular structure. The way the cell worked reminded me of Pops' steel plant. I could remember visiting the plant and being impressed by how well-organized it was. The plant had operations managers, machinists, line workers, delivery men and maintenance men. Each group was minimally impressive on its own, but when coordinated working in harmony, they could produce something extraordinary and beautiful. The human cell was just the same. The cytoplasm, nucleus, mitochondria, cytoskeleton and other organelles each carried out specific functions to make the cell complete. This was all new to me, and I was fascinated. I was also surprised at how well I was picking up the language. The only words I struggled with were the higher-level science words that were new to everyone in class. Mr. Garcia had clearly done a good job prepping me for conversational English.

The final bell rang, and I made my way toward the student pick-up area where Domi had instructed me to meet him. Passing the cafeteria, I saw Johnny out of my peripheral vision and continued as if I hadn't noticed him. Johnny yelled out, "Hey, Brownie, welcome to Aspen High School. I got three acres of grass that needs to be mowed if you're looking for work." Johnny's friends laughed and pointed as I sped past them. I couldn't understand why this guy was being so cruel. I wondered if he had any idea of what I had been through over the summer—losing my parents, leaving my hometown, nearly getting killed.

"How was your first day, son?" Domi asked. I slumped down with my head resting against the dashboard of his Jeep Wagoneer and sighed. "What happened, son?"

"They hate me, Domi. I am a worthless, I will never fit in … NEVER! Screw this school!"

Domi clutched the steering wheel and clenched his teeth. I knew he wanted nothing more than a smooth first day for his nephew who had been through so much over the last couple of months. He searched for the right words to comfort me, but nothing came out. He simply put his hand on my thigh.

Finally, after passing the roundabout on Highway 82, Domi spoke out, "I think I have an idea."

11

BUSHIDO

"It never gets easier; you just get faster."

—Greg LeMond,
three-time winner of the Tour de France

Domi turned left on North 7th Street. "Where are we going?" I asked, noticing we veered off the route we had taken the day before.

"Did you know that your father and I used to dream of becoming successful professional boxers? We would train for hours, read boxing magazines and spar anyone in the neighborhood, regardless of their size."

"Of course, I knew that, Domi."

"Well, unfortunately, when I moved to Aspen, I was saddened to learn that there was no boxing. However, there was something called Aikido."

"Aikido?"

"Yes, Aikido: the way of harmonious spirit. It's a Japanese martial art that trains the body and hones the mind. Aikido practitioners are able to defend themselves while also protecting their attacker from injury. Most importantly, training Aikido forges Bushido spirit."

"What's Bushido?" I asked.

"Bushido means 'way of the warrior.' It was the foundational philosophy and training code of the Japanese Samurai warrior. Bushido spilled into every aspect of the Samurai's life, from martial arts mastery to their moral compass. Did you know that the Japanese Samurai sword took weeks to forge and its creation was considered a sacred art? Multiple craftsman would work on the same sword, repeatedly heating the steel, carefully folding and pounding it with painful precision. The process was never rushed and always performed with care and accuracy. The Samurai's approach to training and life was similar, and it is one of the main reasons it has been memorialized in books and movies going back to the 12th century. After my wife and kids left me, I found Aikido. The discipline, the redirection of physical force and the Aikido philosophy helped me regain my 'bushido' spirit."

We drove past the futuristic tent structure which housed the Aspen Music School, swung left past a concrete and glass structure at the edge of a beautiful meadow and pulled into the Aspen Meadows parking lot. I was immediately flooded with emotion. "I remember this place" I said to Domi. "This is where I found you when I first came to Aspen."

Domingo opened the door to the studio and ceremoniously took off his shoes. I followed. The studio floor was covered in tightly-stretched canvas which created a cloud-like surface. A Japanese flag rested on the east wall and the American flag hung proudly on the opposing wall to the west. A vertical banner with Japanese script was displayed above the office door. As we got closer, I noticed old black and white images of what appeared to be Aikido masters on the office wall. Domi gently rapped on the ajar office door. A stoic man with thick blonde hair, a strong posture and piercing blue eyes came to the door. He reached out and shook Domi's hand.

"Who is this?" the man asked.

"Sensei, I would like you to meet my nephew, Manuel."

"Oss" said the sensei as he hinged forward at his hips and lowered his head.

I looked towards Domi, he nodded his head forward in approval and I tried to mimic what Sensei had said. "Oss," I replied with a strong Tizayuca accent.

"Manny, this is Sensei Tom Gold. He is a famous Aikido master, author of multiple books and a respected community leader, and Sensei, you remember Manuel from the start of the summer?" Domi inquired. "Of course, what brings you gentlemen here today?" asked Tom.

"I think Aikido might be a good experience for Manuel," Domi stated. "He has been through a lot and could use some bushido spirit."

"Do you have an open mind?" Tom asked.

"Yes, sir," I replied.

"How about an open heart?"

"I think so," I replied with less confidence.

"Fantastic, class starts in twenty minutes. Domingo, can you show Manuel to the locker room?" Tom then pulled a gi (the traditional uniform worn by Aikido practitioners) and white belt from his closet. "You know, Manuel, the white belt is the most special and important belt worn by a martial artist. It symbolizes innocence, purity, and most importantly, a new beginning," Tom handed the gi and belt to me. I caught his eyes and offered a slight smile.

Other students began to trickle into the dojo, talking easily with each other as they took off their shoes and prepared for class. After several minutes, Sensei Gold clapped his hands, and the students lined up by rank. The highest rank stood in the front right of the class and I was instructed to take a place in the back, left corner. On this day, Domi would be the third-highest ranking student and fortunate enough to stand directly in front of Sensei. "I would like to start with a meditation to align our minds and calm our spirits," said Tom. The students all knelt, tucked their feet closely together behind them and sat back on their heels. With a soft, confident voice, Tom instructed us to focus on our breath and reflect on what we were grateful for in our lives.

He continued, "Clear your heads and open your minds. We all have worries and concerns. It's time to let go of toxicity and fear, let go of any regrets you might have, and return your focus to the present. Our greatest gift is our human experience, the NOW, and the now isn't possible without our breath. Take a deep inhalation through your nose and follow it with a long, slow exhalation from the mouth. With each breath, sense yourself sinking into a deeper state of calm. Feel your muscles relax around your neck and upper back, imagine tension melting through your mid and lower back and finally into your hips and legs. With each breath, empty your mind, clear your conscience and prepare yourself for growth."

My mind started to wander. He kept saying to slow down, but everything was speeding up for me—my breath, my heart rate, my thoughts. I began to replay the night I lost my parents. I envisioned machine gun rounds lighting up the night sky and heard the dark and sinister voices of Diablo Negro. I started to sweat and twitch. "How long is this stupid drill?" I thought to myself. One minute turned into two, which turned into three. I became flustered and perplexed; I could take it no longer. I jumped up and quickly exited out to the tea room. Domi noticed the commotion and quickly followed me out.

I was pacing nervously in the tea room. "I can't do this, Domi. My mind is racing. Can we just go?" Domi looked disappointed but said nothing. We gathered our gear and went back to the cottage. When we got there, I grabbed my backpack, went straight to my room and slammed the door in frustration.

"I am going out to get us a pizza. I'll be back in a few," bellowed Domi from down the hallway.

Delatori coughed, suddenly drawing Manuel back to the present. "I can see why Aikido meant something special to your uncle," he said.

Manuel nodded. "Yes, it was Aikido that helped him keep his sanity after losing his family. The slow and methodical progress he achieved through martial arts gave him hope that one day he would be at peace, hope that one day he would be a better man, and hope that one day he would win his family back. But on that day, he wasn't thinking about Aikido, he was thinking about the responsibility he now had to me. In some ways, I was a reminder of everything he had lost. I don't claim to be a psychologist, but when I stormed out of the dojo that day, it triggered something deep in him. That's why he wavered."

Raising his eyebrows, Delatori leaned toward Manuel. "Wavered?" he asked. "What do you mean?"

"Later that day, Domingo walked into the Green Turtle Liquor Store and bought a fifth of Jack Daniels. After not drinking for more than three years, it must have been like being reunited with an old friend. Just like that, his sobriety was over."

Delatori lowered his head and sighed in understanding.

"Prior to my arrival in Aspen, Domi had a pretty good routine which was the keystone to his sobriety. He went to Aikido on Tuesdays and Thursdays, AA meetings on Monday and Friday nights, and even joined a bowling league that competed on Saturdays, down valley, in a little town called El Jebel (the Elk). My arrival, although a miracle from God, was disruptive to his routine and brought unique challenges to a single man. In that moment when

I left Aikido practice, Domingo felt like he had failed me. My bad day at school, coupled with a poor first Aikido class, threw him over the edge. Unfortunately, he had one solution that never failed him in times of stress and loss, a go-to that always brought instant comfort, warmth and companionship—barrel-aged, distilled, Tennessee whiskey."

"I have a family member that has struggled with addiction, too. It's one of the hardest things I have ever had to deal with." Delatori remarked and then took another deep breath. "Tell me more about that night."

That night, Domi brought the pizza home and told me he had some work to do in his office and not to disturb him. Right before I headed to bed, I went to the kitchen to get some water and noticed the sliding door open to the porch. I approached the door and heard Domi weeping. Not knowing what to do, I slowly backed up and retreated into my bedroom. As I lay in bed, I closed my eyes and envisioned my mother singing to me. My favorite song was "Duerme Ya," a Spanish version of a Brahms lullaby.

Duerme ya, dulce bebé
Mi capullo de nardo.

Despacito duérmete
como la abeja en la flor.

Duerme ya, dulce bebé
Duerme ya, dulce amor
Dulces sueños tendrás
al oir mi canción.

As I drifted off to sleep, I briefly envisioned myself walking through a field of tall grass, beams of sunlight warmed my face and Summer's delicate hand was intertwined with mine.

Suddenly I heard a loud CRASH!

I sprung upright in bed, and the first thing I thought of was my science lecture earlier in the day, when we discussed the sympathetic "fight or flight" nervous system response.

Hair standing up on my skin: check!

Heart racing: check!

Stomach fluttering: check!

I was experiencing a full-blown sympathetic response.

As I got out of bed and moved slowly towards the hallway, I heard a tremendously loud scratching noise that sounded like someone raking shingles into a pile. I crept towards the kitchen and suddenly stopped, wide-eyed and shaking. Standing in the kitchen was a massive black bear. The bear must have been six feet from snout to rump and every bit of 350 pounds. I was surprised that its fur looked so rough, matted down and scraggly. It didn't look like the postcard pictures Domi had sent me from Aspen when I was younger. I stood there, unable to move, and watched as it tried to pry open the trash cabinet underneath the kitchen sink.

I opened my mouth to scream to Domi, but nothing came out. My heart was beating so violently, I was certain the bear could hear it through my rib cage. I tried to inch back towards my room, but as I pushed off on the wood floor a loud "creak" echoed down the hallway. The bear paused and looked at me with dark, motionless eyes. I held my breath for what seemed like an eternity. Then, as quickly as it appeared, the bear turned nonchalantly towards the porch and walked back out through the same sliding door it had come in. If I didn't know better, I would say he was swaggering like he owned the cabin.

Still rooted to the floor of the hallway, I stood gasping for air. That's when I noticed Domi out of the corner of my eye. He was curled up in an embryonic position on the couch, completely oblivious to the bear's commotion. It had knocked over the kitchen table and raked its razor-sharp claws across the kitchen cabinets, making a nails-on-chalkboard screech, yet Domi just lay there in a stupor. I yelled to him, but he didn't move. Heart still racing and in disbelief of what had just happened, I walked over and tried to wake Domi. I shook his shoulder and said in an authoritative tone "Domi, wake up," but he was out like a light. I grabbed a goose down comforter from the hall closet to gently drape over him, then I closed and locked the porch door where the bear had entered. That's when I noticed a bottle of whiskey laying empty on the porch, and I started to put everything together. My abrupt departure from Aikido must have triggered him, reminding him of all those who had left him, or maybe he was missing my parents as much as me. I slumped back to my room feeling responsible for what had happened, and it took a long time for me to fall back to sleep.

The next morning upon waking, I decided to show my appreciation for all my uncle had done for me over the last couple of months. I gathered eggs, chorizo, peppers, avocado, cheddar cheese and salsa and began to prepare my mother's famous Mexican eggs. Domi got a whiff of my cooking and abruptly lifted his head up like a deer that just heard a loud noise in the woods.

"Domi, what gives?" I said, smiling. "Last night a 350-pound bear was tearing this place apart and you didn't budge, but with one smell of fresh chorizo, you jump to attention."

"Bear?" Domingo asked, sitting up a little higher.

"Yes, last night a massive bear broke in, tore the place apart and almost killed me! Okay, maybe he didn't almost kill me, but I definitely feared for my life!" I responded.

Shocked, Domingo jumped up off the couch. As his foot came down, it landed on a fallen lampshade, crushing it flat as a pancake. Struggling to get his foot free and stay balanced, he took another couple of steps toward the kitchen before he banged his right knee into a table that must have been overturned by our four-legged visitor from the night before. "Ouch!" he yelped, grabbing his right leg with one hand and steadying himself against the counter with the other. "Damn, it looks like a tornado went through here," Domi said as he looked around, surveying the damage.

"Yeah, a tornado you slept through."

Domingo made his way through the wreckage, turned the table upright and rummaged through the cabinets for aspirin. "Did I mention it's important to keep the doors closed and locked here in Aspen?" Domingo stated with a wry smile.

"Noted for next time." I responded.

Domi put a pot of coffee on the stove and came down to sit next to me. "I'm sorry, Manuel," Domi said as he looked intently into my eyes. He sighed deeply, reached for my hand and said, "Let's pray." Together we bowed our heads as Domi began, "Lord, you have carried me through the hardest of times. You have accompanied me during the loneliness and shouldered me in the darkness. Lead me from the emptiness and despair of addiction, and please do not give up on me." As he finished, he gave my hand a firm squeeze and once again looked apologetically into my eyes.

12

BODY BLOW

"It's a little like wrestling a gorilla.
You don't quit when you're tired.
You quit when the gorilla is tired."
—Fausto Coppi, Italian cyclist
and international champion during WWII

"By the way, I'm not driving you to school today," Domingo told me after breakfast.

"Well, how do you expect me to get there?" I replied curtly.

"Follow me."

Domi led me to a work shed behind the cabin. The shed was rustic, but full of well-organized gear. On the south side was a large peg-board with an expansive array of tools. The north wall housed two lawnmowers, a weed-whacker, a Shop-Vac, edger and blower. In the back of the shed, by the workbench, was a collection of sporting gear, including three pairs of skis, some tennis racquets and two snowboards. Domi moved the snowboards aside, uncovering something gloriously familiar. Leaning up against the workbench was a 1986 Colnago master road racing bike.

"DOMI, DO YOU KNOW WHAT THIS IS?" I shouted with unbridled enthusiasm.

"Yeah, it's a bike," Domi replied.

"No, sir, this is not just a bike. This is a slice of HEAVEN! It was featured in *VeloNews* two years ago when Giuseppe Saronni won the Giro d'Italia riding this very bike," I reported to Domi. "I have read all about this bike. It was designed to be an improvement on the 'Mexico' which had been Colnago's top model before."

"Was it better than The Red Rocket?" Delatori interrupted with an inquisitive smile.

"Better than The Red Rocket!" Manuel said with exultation. "The Red Rocket was amazing, just like a first girlfriend. But no one marries their first girlfriend. This thing was worthy of a ring. The bike had evergreen tubing and profile sections designed by

Gilberto Columbo, the famous Italian engineer who started the Gilco design firm and was instrumental in designing cars like the Maserati Tipo. The frame was designed to improve stiffness for hill climbs and sprints and reduce mechanical strain. It had a low-profile leather seat that was designed for speed and garnished with gold rivets." Manuel paused, letting his words catch up with his memory. "The best part of this bike was its Campagnolo C-Record components. The components, or groupset, of a bike are everything that make you stop and go including the drivetrain, shifters and brakes. And this bike had the absolute finest. At that time, there were two main component manufacturers—the Italian company, Campagnolo and the Japanese company, Shimano. Although Shimano made top of the line Dura-Ace groupings, most of the purists in the sport preferred the highly-coveted C-record groupings made by Campagnolo." Manuel grinned in happiness as he described the Colnago in vivid detail, and then finished his description. "Of course, the most striking aspect of this bike was its color—metallic red."

"You really are a geek when it comes to bikes," Delatori said in jest.

"Thank you," Manuel responded emphatically, dropping his head and sweeping his arm out to the side as if taking a dramatic bow.

"So, what's the deal? How did your uncle get a hold of such a gem?" asked Delatori.

"It's probably the only good thing that came out of my uncle's addiction," reported Manuel.

"I'll never forget one specific letter your father sent me in which he described your love for biking," Domi informed me. "He said you would ride to and from school daily, then ride up the mountains of Tizayuca after school and then ride in the streets in front of your house until Rosina would bark at you, 'NO MAS,' from the front door of your apartment. José saw something in you that he saw in himself when he picked up boxing gloves. He recognized a greatness in you that would manifest itself only with the help of a bike. I never forgot this letter," Domi said. "This bike belongs to you, son."

"Do you know how expensive this bike is, Domi? Where did you get it?"

"The bike was given to me by a friend who I sponsored in AA, Antonio. Antonio is a chef and avid rider who claims I saved his life. The only way he could repay me was with this bike. Actually, I tried to refuse the gift, and he was so offended, we almost got into a fist fight over the whole thing. Long story short, the bike is mine, and now it's YOURS!"

"REGRESO DE EL COHETE DE ROJO—return of The Red Rocket!" I screamed.

Dom reached out to give me a high five while I went in for the "bro shake." We met awkwardly in the middle of the failed attempt, and both began to laugh.

I arrived at school on The Red Rocket 2.0 with a newfound enthusiasm. No matter how cruel other kids treated me at school, I once again had purpose. I once again had a mission. I once again had freedom. When I took my seat in class, Summer was there to greet me with a smile.

Like most teenagers, I seemed to walk through life mostly oblivious to what was going on around me. However, when it came to Summer, I noticed everything—what she wore, how she styled her hair, the smell of her perfume, and even if her shoelaces were tied evenly. On this day, Summer was wearing distressed jeans with holes in them, nude-colored sandals and a pink tank top that had a peace sign on the front.

"Buenos días, Manuel," she said.

"You speak Spanish?" I replied.

"Yeah, I spent six months in an exchange program in Spain. It's a beautiful language," she said.

Smiling contently, I settled into my chair as Mr. Hightower started the day's lesson.

At lunch, I sat by myself and enjoyed some of the most amazing cafeteria food I could imagine. I don't remember eating like this in Tizayuca and didn't even recognize some of the names of the menu items: barbeque chicken sandwich, corn on the cob, Greek salad, chocolate mousse? I might not have known the names of the food, but I recognized greatness when I tasted it. I was so immersed in eating this four-course cafeteria meal that I didn't notice Johnny staring at me maliciously from two tables away. As I got up to head out for break period, Johnny and his minions followed.

"Sorry we didn't have rice and beans on the menu today, bro, but if you want to go down and eat with the custodial staff, I'm sure they will have your kind of food."

I had been quiet long enough. "Screw you, blondie," I replied.

Johnny, surprised to hear me speak, clenched his right fist, coiled his body and threw a massive right-hand punch to my stomach. I crumbled to the ground and began wheezing as the other students looked on in shock. Many kids stood around laughing, but Summer, who witnessed the tail end of the altercation, ran over to console me.

Still gasping for breath and too embarrassed to look at Summer, I grabbed my backpack, raced towards the bike rack behind the school and took off. I couldn't go home as I knew Domi wouldn't tolerate me ditching school. As I exited the parking lot, I looked up and saw a massive bird with hooked beak and bright red tail feathers, something I had never seen in Mexico. Its wings must have stretched four feet across. It flew with power and grace, and as it veered north towards a road sign that read "Maroon Bells," I decided to follow. Within minutes of riding, I passed a gate just beyond the T-Lazy-7 Ranch, and I was finally alone.

A mild crosswind swept through my hair. The hawk let out a loud raspy "kee-eeeee-arrr" and I closed my eyes. I envisioned the road to the cross, high atop my village. I remembered the solitude, the late day sun warming my face and the freedom of riding my bike. An image of my mother and father atop the Sierra Gorda mountain range appeared. They were smiling, holding hands and gazing directly towards me.

Finding a higher gear, I rose from my saddle and drove towards the ground like I was punching the earth with the balls of my feet. My legs began to burn, and my chest expanded and compressed like an accordion. My oversized backpack, filled with books, felt like a gorilla on my back. The thin mountain air, coupled with the high level of exertion, was disorienting. My vision became narrow, all I could see was the summit. I had not felt this level of pain, exhaustion and discomfort since riding switchback twenty-two. I LOVED IT!

Six miles later, I rolled up to a pristine lake at the basin of two huge, jagged peaks. My heart was pounding from the exertion, and as I got off my bike and started to slowly walk around,

I began to gather my senses. The peaks were radiant, spectacular and awe-inspiring. Although I loved the Sierra Gorda range, the colors here were unique and breathtaking. Brightly colored wildflowers lay amidst dense field grass that was gently swaying in the midday breeze. The distinctive maroon and amber rock faces of the mountains were in sharp contrast to the rich green tree leaves that gently danced in the wind. These mountains looked as if they had been sculpted over millions of years and hand-painted by the gods.

I noticed a group of cyclists just to my left. Clad in Lycra from head to toe, they wore fancy helmets and weird-looking cleated shoes. The group of cyclists were staring at me wearing expressions of disbelief. Without a helmet or sunglasses, wearing jeans and carrying an over-sized backpack, I must have looked lost.

"Want some water?" asked one of the cyclists. I accepted the water bottle and took several grateful gulps.

"First time to the Maroon Bells?" asked one of the riders. I smiled, laid my bike down and without answering, walked towards the lake.

Although it was small, the reflective lake was breathtaking. Surrounded by groves of aspen, spruce and conifer trees, the water glistened as a light breeze brushed across its surface, sending ripples across its face. The two massive peaks at the lake's backdrop huddled together like a happily-married couple, the reflective pool at their feet amplifying the mountains and sky. It all reminded me of how small I was; how small we all were in the universe. A smile came across my face. I had forgotten how much I loved nature and being outdoors. For the first time I was at peace in my new home.

13

FLOW LIKE WATER

"The bicycle has a soul. If you succeed to love it, it will give you emotions you will never forget."

—Mario Cipollini,
Italian cyclist known for his sprinting prowess

On the ride home, I turned north off Highway 82 and tried to find my way back towards Red Mountain. Without realizing where I was, I noticed that I was passing the Aspen Meadows. I had remembered what Pops said years ago about wronging someone. "Manny, if you have ever let someone down, a simple, yet genuine apology will restore faith and build character." My father's words echoed in my head as I thought about running out of Tom's class the day before. I veered into the Meadows and placed The Red Rocket into an artfully-designed bike rack on the east side of the complex.

Approaching the dojo, I heard beautiful Japanese flute music coming from within.

I could see Tom engaging in some type of pattern through a mirror that reflected into the dojo. He was alone and the lights were off. He was holding a wooden sword and moved with the grace of a ballerina and the power of a waterfall. "How was this possible?" I thought to myself. Tom wore a loose-fitting white top and a traditional black skirt that made a crisp whoosh as he moved across the floor. It reminded me of making my bed, back in Tizayuca; of throwing the top sheet into the air and whipping it open with purpose.

Just then Tom caught my reflection and held his pose in a low defensive posture.

"Manuel, please come in."

"Tom, I wanted to apologize for running out of class the other day."

"No worries, my friend. The meditation practice is one of the hardest parts of Aikido," he paused, looking me directly in the eye, "but it's also the most valuable."

"Why is it so important?" I asked.

"If you can't control your mind, you can't control your body. It's not just about martial arts. It's analogous to life." Walking toward his office, Tom motioned for me to follow.

"Come here. I want to show you something." In his office, he pointed to a black and white photo on the wall. "This was my Sensei, Terry Dobson. Terry was the first American Aikido master to be trained by the Japanese. He once disarmed three robbers in a Japanese train station all by himself."

"That's crazy," I said. "How did he do it—foot sweeps, rapid punching, leg kicks?"

"No," replied Tom. "With words. You see, Aikido is not about combat, it's about avoiding conflict. It's not about separation, it's about unification." He clearly hadn't met Johnny, I thought to myself as the memory of getting punched in the stomach a few hours prior resurfaced.

He led me back out into the dojo. "Punch me," said Tom.

I shook my head. "I can't do that. I wouldn't feel right."

"Don't worry, Manuel. Punch at me."

Hesitating just a moment longer, I reared back and threw a right overhand punch at Tom's head. It was a punch I had seen Pops throw hundreds of times in his home gym. Tom stepped to the left, and with a low-to-high circular motion, redirected my punch, throwing me off balance.

"Again," Tom said.

Once again, I reared back, this time aiming at Tom's stomach, trying to trick him. Tom performed the same block, but this time with a high-to-low circular arch. As he redirected my body shot, he somehow ended up behind me, put his arm around my shoulder, and gave me a hug.

"Bruce Lee once said, 'flow like water.' You put water into a cup, it becomes the cup. You put water into a bottle, it becomes the bottle. You put water into a teapot, it becomes the teapot. Now, water can flow." He moved both arms in a beautifully synchronized circular motion. "Or water can crash." At that moment, he delivered a right-hand palm strike to the floor that literally shook teacups on a table at the side of the dojo. "Be water, my friend." I stood silently, in awe.

Tom walked back towards his office, turned toward me, and said, "See you tomorrow for class."

I hadn't been this excited since Pops had signed me up for guitar lessons on my tenth birthday. One of his coworkers had offered to teach me guitar in exchange for car maintenance work. I learned Spanish and flamenco guitar and loved honoring my roots and expanding my talents. Even though it was not of my culture, Aikido felt the same way, and I couldn't wait to begin.

However, the first Aikido class didn't go as I had expected. The lesson that first day was on footwork and the importance of balance. Toward the end of class, Tom said something in Japanese, and all the black belts formed a line on the west side of the dojo. There were five of them, both men and women, of different ages and different sizes. “Time to see how well you learned,” he commanded, which was Tom’s catchphrase every night before sparring.

The drill was to attack the black belt with the technique of your choice, but to end up on your feet in perfect balance following the attack. I first lined up against a sixteen-year-old girl. I threw a front snap kick, which she easily caught. She proceeded to sweep my rear leg and put me on my tush. I then faced Bobby, a construction worker from Carbondale. I went with my Pops’ signature punch, the overhand right. Once again, my punch was blocked, and I was spun around, got my feet tangled up, and you guessed it—tush! One by one, I fought and fell. Not once was I able to stay in an upright posture. With two loud claps of Tom’s hands, the black belts lined up again, bowed toward their opponents and class was over.

I glanced over at Tom with a look of disgust on my face. Tom looked back and in a wise guy voice said, “How do you like it so far?” I grabbed my bag and huffed toward the parking lot. Tom caught up to me just as I was mounting my bike.

“I SUCK!”

“Manuel, let me ask you something. Have you ever learned something brand new?”

“Yeah, I guess.”

"What was it?"

"Guitar," I replied.

"Well, how good were you on day one?"

"Terrible, I guess."

"Exactly," said Tom. "See you tomorrow."

14

GRIND

"No hour of life is lost that is spent in the saddle."

—Winston Churchill,
British Prime Minister (1940-1945, 1951-1955)

I now had a new routine. Every day after school, I would chase what I had learned in ecology class was a red-tailed hawk, up to the Maroon Bells. When I came back down, I went to Aikido. Pops used to always profess, "A daily routine turns a boy into a man," and that's how I felt. Besides, the only way I could keep my mind off my parents was to grind. For the next couple of weeks, I did nothing but study, ride my new bike, practice Aikido, and, of course, pine after Summer.

My favorite class was anatomy & physiology, where we studied the human body. I learned about the heart's ability to deliver oxygenated blood throughout the body and how more red blood cells bind to oxygen at altitude, enhancing performance. I learned about how stroke volume, the amount of blood pumped through the left ventricle of the heart each beat, can be altered through aggressive training. I learned about lactate threshold and how the body adapts to intense training by minimizing the impact of lactate on the muscles. I had a thirst for knowledge when it came to the human body and wanted to learn everything I could about enhancing my performance. My English at this point was superb, and I now had the confidence to speak up in class and ask numerous questions.

I also liked political science. My teacher, Chief Akecheta (which means "fighter"), was a Native American Ute Indian and a real badass. Chief Akecheta was an important figure in Aspen, an area first inhabited by the Utes. The chief had been lecturing on a newly-enacted immigration policy called The Immigration Reform and Control Act of 1986. The Reform Act made it illegal to knowingly recruit and hire illegal immigrants, required employers to attest to their employees' legal status, and established penalties for those employing illegals. My political science class often had debates over this policy, making me extremely uncomfortable. Johnny Roberts, who was a strong proponent of the policy, would often get into debates with Chief Akecheta.

One day in class, Johnny said that illegal immigrants should never be allowed in America as they are "murderers and rapists," which seemed to get the teacher's attention. "Johnny, let me tell you a story of my people, the Ute Indians," replied Chief Akecheta in an authoritative, scholarly tone. "We have lived on this land since the beginning of time. As a people, we have developed a unique relationship with the environment. We never owned the land we lived on; the land owned us. We lived for hundreds of years in harmony, balance and peace until the Europeans arrived. They brought with them cholera, smallpox and other diseases. They enslaved our people, took our land, had their way with our mothers and sisters and murdered those of us that showed defiance. You need to be careful about who you refer to as murderers and rapists in my classroom." There was dead silence and Johnny, speechless, looked at the floor. I cheered wildly in my head, grateful for at least one ally at Aspen High School.

I would often discuss immigration policy and the Reform Act with my uncle. "I don't want to go back to Mexico. I want to stay here with you," I would plead to Domingo. "I will get straight A's. I will stay out of trouble. I will get a job and work hard. I will do whatever it takes to become an American citizen," I promised.

"Keep doing what you're doing, Manuel." Domingo said. "I will look into your citizenship, and yes, a job would be good. I have a friend who works at La Cantina. I will check into employment for you. Don't worry, son, I won't let anyone take you away from me. You're all I have." Domi had a huge responsibility taking care of me which took a toll on him. I would occasionally find empty liquor bottles hidden in the bottom of the kitchen trash can. I tried to ignore it the best that I could as things were going fairly well, and I didn't want anything bad to happen to Dominic.

My riding was quickly improving. I often played a game called pasar los turistas. I would count the number of tourists I could pass on my way up to the Maroon Bells. My record was thirty-five. I started to fiddle with my body position on the bike. I noticed that by shifting my weight forward, backward or even standing up off the saddle, I could relax some muscles while activating others. By alternating body positions, I seemed to fatigue much less, and discovered that I had a knack for the "backseat" position.

Positional changes were used by all the great riders, but the backseat position was reserved for the true grinders. It is a position of commitment, a position of deliverance, a position of pain and a position I loved.

I remembered reading about famous hill climbers like Fausto Coppi, "Champion of Champions," in *VeloNews*. He would use the backseat position as he challenged the best of the professional bikers between 1946 and 1954. The "Angel of the Mountains," Charly Gaul, was also famous for using the backseat position. He was known for sand-bagging the flat stages of the Tour de France, only to get in the back seat and demoralize his competitors in the mountains.

My Aikido was also improving. I found it to be a metaphor for life. "The art is in simplicity," Tom would often say, quoting Bruce Lee. "Strip away the non-essentials until the truth is revealed." I got accustomed to slowing down my physiology; my heart rate, my respiratory rate, and seeing my opponents' attacks before they occurred. I was now able to spar and compete against all the black belts in the class except one—James, from Carbondale. James had been with Tom for four years. He had a wide frame, solid base, and smooth, effortless delivery in his techniques. James was the perfect opponent for me. He took me under his wing and mentored me. He had a knack for pushing newer students to the limits. On rare occasions, I would catch James with an overhand right during sparring. I imagined a smile appearing on Pop's face in heaven. I loved my routine. It grounded me, helped me focus and gave me purpose. I was missing only one thing—Summer.

15

CRUZ

"When your legs scream stop and your lungs are bursting,
that's when it starts.
That's the hurt locker. Winners love it there."

—Chris McCormack,
two-time winner of the Ironman Word Championship

Although my uncle worked for them, I had yet to meet any of the family that lived in the Red Mountain mansion. I often came home after dark and used the back entrance to the cottage. All I knew of the family was that Mr. Campbell, the owner, was a right-wing Colorado State Representative and had recently voted in favor of The Immigration Reform and Control Act. Domingo would often mutter spiteful things under his breath about Mr. Campbell but was also smart enough not to bite the hand that fed him.

One Saturday afternoon, Domi needed help preparing the grounds for a big political rally Mr. Campbell was having at the residence. I worked diligently, aligning parking cones, organizing tables and blowing debris from the driveway. As more cars entered the residence, the 1984 Bruce Springsteen hit, "Born in the USA," began to blare from a P.A. system, and some anti-immigration signs were lifted into the air by spectators.

Dom and I finished working and stood around the corner watching the rally in disbelief. The crowd grew to over 150 people in the next hour and eventually, a town car arrived with a very special delivery. Mr. Campbell greeted the car and opened the rear passenger door. Out stepped Summer.

With a thunderous roar from the crowd, Mr. Campbell grasped Summer's hand and kissed her cheek warmly. Lightning coursed through my veins, and my heart felt as if it was being compressed by the weight of thirty stones. "Summer is Mr. Campbell's daughter?" I asked Domi with a mixture of surprise and disgust.

"How do you know Summer?"

"From school. I had no idea she was Mr. Campbell's daughter," I answered.

Mr. Campbell wasn't necessarily a bad man. We were just so dissimilar. I guess in some ways he represented the American dream of opulence, decadence and excess. He had clearly raised a beautiful and respectful daughter, worked hard to obtain a prominent position in the government, and lived in one of the most beautiful houses I had ever seen. I just didn't understand why he was so against immigrants. Wasn't it immigrants that built this nation? Did he care about his Mexican employees like my uncle who arduously took care of his property? Did he see who we were as a people: our work ethic, our love of family, our humility? Would he have me deported or jailed if he found out about my illegal status? Most importantly, did his daughter share his beliefs? As Summer stood next to her father in solidarity my lovesick heart quickly filled with confusion.

The single most magnificent woman I had ever seen was not who I thought she was. Domi saw me pacing behind the cottage, fists clenched, and nostrils flared. "Are you okay, son?" he asked.

"Do I look okay?" I snapped back. This was a feeling I had yet to experience in my seventeen years on this earth. I wondered if this was what Pops experienced before he stepped into a boxing ring. A primal rage coursed through me. My internal organs twisted into knots, and my head felt compressed, as if it was being squeezed by a vice. My heart raced and I couldn't stop moving. I began to feel unhinged.

"I have to get out of here," I thought to myself. I needed to get far away from the sign bearers, away from the Congressman and away from Summer.

I ran back to the cottage and I'm not sure why, but I swiped Mama's cross pendant from the desk lamp and put it around my neck. Wearing jeans, a loose t-shirt and tennis shoes, I grabbed my bike and rode towards the only place I knew that could calm my spirit—the place where the hawks fly, the rock radiates maroon and the water glistens. My brain seemed to shut down, sound disappeared, and my vision tunneled. The only thing that I could truly feel was my connection with the bike.

As I rode, an image sequence began to play in my head like a movie on the big screen. I saw the Diaz family shake in distress as they were closed-up in a crate, the unforgettable crackling of gun fire appeared as orange flashes of phosphorescent light, and then I saw myself from above, running for my life into the abyss.

My mother's necklace gently bounced off my chest like a metronome, helping me keep a rapid pedal cadence. Unlike the Sierra Gorda range, the pavement was smooth and consistent, and my riding felt effortless. Ahead of me was an echelon of bikers on their way up to the Maroon Bells. One of the riders yelled something to me as I flew by, but I was locked in and failed to respond. I barely noticed the group as I punched past them.

Delatori laughed aloud, snapping Manuel back to the present. "That's incredible," he said. "I would love to have seen the look on their faces when you blew past them wearing jeans."

Manuel laughed as well. "Me, too. Of course, they were behind me, so I couldn't see the look on their faces."

Both men smiled. "I later learned that the group was the seven-time State Champion Aspen High School Cycling Team, coached by Chris Carmouche. He was a member of the first U.S. Cycling Team to compete in the Tour de France earlier that year. Chris was following the team in a vehicle providing extra water, energy bars, replacement wheels and coaching tips. Coach Carmouche later told me that when he and his assistant witnessed me rip by their A-Team like they were standing still, they looked at one another like they had just seen an alien."

Delatori chuckled again, "Little did they know, you actually were an alien."

Manuel, grinning widely, nodded and continued.

My new bike was smoother, lighter, and twice as powerful as The Red Rocket. After four years of hammering up the Sierra Gorda mountain range on an antiquated, limited gear Schwinn Stingray, my Colnago felt like a NASA-designed rocket ship.

Sustaining 96 rpms in an aggressive gear, by the time I reached the top, I had put significant distance between myself and the Aspen Cycling Team.

I set my bike against the fence and stared up toward the Bells. I felt light, elevated and euphoric. The sun, which had just descended behind the mountain ridge, thrust pink and orange hues of light across the dome of the sky. The Aspen High School bike team and Coach Carmouche pulled in about forty-five seconds behind me. Johnny, the team's captain, was so fatigued that he struggled to dislodge his right cleat from his bike pedal and nearly toppled over behind me. Surprised by the loud scraping of his cleat on the concrete, I turned to see the entire team staring at me.

Coach Carmouche got out of the truck and studied me from head to toe. I originally couldn't figure out why he was so focused on my tennis shoes, but I noticed his team were all wearing expensive-looking cycling cleats.

Coach Carmouche's eyes shifted upward; my baggy blue jeans contrasted starkly against his team's tightly sewn and brightly-branded Lycra bike shorts. My loose-fitting shirt, which I had failed to tuck in prior to the ride, had been flapping in the wind throughout the ascent.

"Who are you?" asked Coach Carmouche.

"I'm Manuel Cruz Delgado," I said emphatically.

"CRUZ is right. You just 'cruised' by some of the best high school riders in the state wearing tennis shoes and jeans."

I shrugged my shoulders. "I guess I was in a zone," I replied. Johnny watched as Coach Carmouche, clearly impressed, eyed me with curiosity.

"How 'bout you join us on the Aspen High School Cycling Team? We are training for Nationals, and I think you could really help our team."

"No, thanks," I replied. "I train Aikido. But good luck at Nationals." I added with a slight wave.

I mounted my bike and offered Johnny a smug smile as I passed the team. I pulled my mother's necklace out from under my shirt and kissed it. "I will never leave your side again, Mama," I thought to myself as I headed back home.

16

RETRIBUTION

"If the constellations had been named in the twentieth century, I suppose we would look up and see bicycles."

—Carl Sagan,
astrophysicist best known for popularizing astronomy

The next day at school, as I was retrieving books from my locker between political science and language arts, I saw Johnny and his best friend Chuckie approaching from down the hallway. Judging by the look on Johnny's face, I could tell he wasn't happy about getting shown up on his bike the day before.

As Johnny distracted me, Chuckie snuck behind me and assumed a position on all fours directly behind my legs. "Great ride yesterday." Johnny said as he forcefully pushed against my chest. I toppled backwards over Chuckie, dropping my books, but somehow rolled out of the fall into a perfect staggered fighting stance, facing Johnny.

"Ready to eat another one of my punches?" Johnny snorted.

"Please stop, Johnny. I don't want to get in trouble," I replied.

"It's a little too late for that, taco head!"

Johnny threw a right cross towards my stomach, the same punch he had knocked me down with before, but this time I blocked his punch with a downward circular motion of my right arm. Johnny fell forward, landing like a sea turtle on the ground. He got up, even more agitated. This time he grabbed his backpack, which was full of heavy books, and swung it towards my head. I ducked and pushed Johnny on his trailing shoulder, which rotated him and sent him flying head-first into the lockers. Johnny tried to get up, but his head had directly contacted the lockers, which left him dizzy and bleeding from his forehead.

"Get up, Johnny," Chuckie urged.

Pushing her way through the crowd, Summer—who had witnessed the whole thing—appeared. "What's going on, Johnny? Why would you attack Manuel like that?" she said.

Johnny peered up with a blank look on his face as blood trickled from his forehead.

I interjected, "I might have a different skin color from you, Johnny, but I am not much different from you. I do homework like you, I have hopes and dreams like you, and I feel pain just like you." I gathered Johnny's books and placed them in his pack, except for one book that I couldn't fit in. Looking down I noticed the title, "Where Do We Go From Here," Dr. Martin Luther King's 1967 benchmark book dealing with racial equality and social justice that had been assigned by Chief Akecheta earlier that week. "You might want to do some more reading." I quipped, as I handed him the book.

Just then, the English teacher came barreling out from his room to find out what all the commotion was about. Mr. Lyman took one look at Johnny's bloody face, grabbed me by the arm and dragged me to the principal's office. Summer tried to stop him, but it was to no avail.

This was not good. Johnny was a star athlete, very popular at school and now a bloody mess. I wasn't just concerned about school, I worried about Domi. Would this throw him off course again with his drinking? Would Sensei be disappointed with me that I used his teachings to hurt someone? Or worse, would this be reported to the immigration authorities and get me deported?

After being briefed by Mr. Lyman, Principal Yates opened his office door and called me in. “We don’t get in fights in Aspen. I know you have been through a lot in the last few months, but this is an environment of the highest civility and grace.” I tried to interject but was quickly interrupted by Principal Yates. “I don’t want to hear any excuses, Manuel. I heard Johnny was a bloody mess; I might have no other option but to suspend you,” he said. My brow began to sweat, and my hands were shaking. The principal began pacing with his hands in his pockets and a disappointed look on his face. Coach Carmouche, who was walking by, saw me in the office and stuck his head in the office door.

“What’s going on here?” asked Coach Carmouche.

“Our new student thinks it’s okay to go around beating up your team captain. He’s about to take an extended break so he can think about his actions.” replied Principal Yates.

Coach Carmouche asked the principal if they could speak privately for a moment. They stepped out of the office while I waited in agony. The door was closed so I couldn’t hear what they were saying, but it sounded heated. After several minutes, they came back in. By this time, I had worked myself up into an anxious mess and was nearly in tears. “Manuel, we might have a solution,” Principal Yates said, as he gave Coach Carmouche the floor.

"Good news, bad news, Cruz. Principal Yates agreed not to suspend you, but you're gonna have to practice more than Aikido now."

"What's that supposed to mean?" I replied nervously.

"It means that if you want to avoid suspension, you're going to have to join an after-school program like robotics, debate or participate on one of the sports team. I am willing to give you a second chance, but only if you get more involved with school." Principal Yates explained.

Coach Carmouche jumped in, "I imagine you're not that good at cycling, but if you're interested, meet me and the team at the upper parking lot tomorrow after school with your bike. Of course, you can always do robotics," the coach said as he lurched out of the office doing his best imitation of a robot. Still traumatized from the day's events, I just sat there with a blank look on my face, unable to answer. Suddenly, Coach popped his head back in the office, "Oh, and wear something other than jeans this time." With a quick wink and a smile, he ducked out of the door and disappeared.

17

TIME TRIAL TUESDAY

"The key is to be able to endure psychologically. When you're not riding well, you think, why suffer?"

—Greg LeMond,
three-time winner of the Tour de France

"I am assuming you didn't have to think long about what after-school activity you wanted to engage in," Delatori said, shifting positions in his chair with a smirk on his face.

"Well, considering I didn't even know what robotics was and had never debated in my life, yes, the decision was easy." Manuel replied.

"Coach Carmouche didn't know if I would show up or not, but of course, I did, and I was in for an epic surprise. Once a year, the Aspen High School Cycling Team engaged in a rite of passage that Coach Carmouche had started years earlier: Time Trial

Tuesday. Time Trial Tuesday was held prior to the first race of each season and determined the strongest riders on the team, as well as the team captain for that year. The captain has the best chance of winning races for the team and is supported in various ways by the secondary riders, called domestiques. Each domestique has a specific job. Some teammates shield the captain from opponents, others allow the captain to draft off them, conserving energy for strategic sprints or hill climbs. Other teammates reel in breakaways from rival teams and try to push them back toward the pack. Regardless of the job, the goal for the team is to have one or two of their strongest riders at the front of the pack for the final sprint. Time Trial Tuesday would determine Aspen's best and grant one or two riders preferential treatment throughout the entire season," Manuel said.

"You must have been a shoo-in, right?" Delatori asked.

"Not so fast, Mark. The time trial is a brutal event in which racers are tested, mentally and physically. Often referred to as the 'race of truth,' riders face the grueling task of pushing themselves as they ride alone, with no one to pace them, no domestique to shield them, and no food or water support. Racing a time trial is like standing naked in front of a mirror; nothing else is as revealing. Also, I didn't know the course; where to push or when to lay-back and coast. So, to answer your question, I knew I had a really good chance of winning, but no, I was not a shoo-in." Manuel said.

"This is getting good. Tell me how it went down," implored Delatori.

So, Coach Carmouche deployed riders from the high school in two-minute intervals on a course that wrapped around the town, up Highway 82 to a gate on a high mountain pass that crossed the Continental Divide and back to the school. Although the course wasn't long, riding alone, battling headwinds, trying to find proper pacing, and the pressure of winning made this day one of the hardest challenges of the year.

"Okay, boys, it's GO TIME!" Coach looked around at the team who seemed eager to be labeled "Top Gun," yet apprehensive about the pain that was about to ensue. "Where's Cruz?" I heard Coach belt out as I approached from around the backside of the building.

"He's not gonna show. He doesn't have the balls!" bellowed Johnny as I rounded the corner and popped into view. I am not sure what was more satisfying, receiving a second chance to stay in school or the look of disgust on Johnny's face when I showed up. I could hear Coach whispering to his assistant, "This just got interesting."

"You're in luck, Cruz. Today is Time Trial Tuesday, essentially the first race of the season. I see you found some shorts," Coach mentioned as he looked down to see me wearing the exact same jeans I had on the day before. The only difference was that now they were cut off above the knees. "Come to my truck, I have something for you." Coach Carmouche gestured for me to follow him. From the back of his truck, he retrieved a white Giro helmet and handed it to me.

"Here it comes," one of the other riders on the team leaned over and whispered to me.

"Here what comes?" I asked.

"Coach's game day speech. Did you know Coach is a legend in Aspen? He competed on the US National Cycling team from 1978 to 1984, racing amongst American legends like Andy Hampsten and Alexi Grewal for Team 7-Eleven.

"Hey, I've read about those guys in *VeloNews*. Isn't Andy Hampsten the only American to ever win the Giro d'Italia?" I replied.

"You are correct, and coach is equally as good, he even raced in the Tour de France earlier this year. As good a rider as he is, he's even more passionate about coaching. If Coach Carmouche can't get you fired up, you're dead inside," the rider said as he reached his hand out to shake mine. "I'm Stretch."

Before I could respond, we were startled by a loud THUD as Coach jumped up on the tailgate of his truck.

"Gentlemen, there are moments in your life that will change the fabric of your character forever; moments that require grit, determination and indomitable spirit; moments that don't just test you physically and mentally, but that reach into your hearts and souls demanding answers; moments that are short in duration, yet echo an eternity; moments that literally define who you are as a human being. Gentlemen, this is one of those moments."

I was mesmerized by Coach's words. When Coach delivered the line, "Gentlemen, this is one of those moments," he looked directly into my eyes as if granting me permission to be extraordinary. Although my parents had empowered me, they did it in a loving and unconditional way. Sensei also facilitated my development as an athlete, but it was more in a philosophical, introspective fashion. This was different, I was being ordered to test myself and determine who I was in the fabric of my soul.

Slater was first up to depart from the high school parking lot, followed by Ben, Christian, Bobby (aka "Stretch" for his 6' 4" frame), Zeth, Kevin, Paul, Johnny (last year's winner), and finally me, bringing up the rear. As I waited for his signal, Coach Carmouche leaned in and gave me some last-minute advice. "This is a race of consistency, Cruz. Don't go out too fast. Find your pace and rhythm. Keep the r-p-ms high and find your demon."

"Demon? What do you mean?" I asked.

"Everyone has something that haunts them, something that is visceral, something that ignites a fire within their belly. Finding it is like finding gold," said Coach. "Okay, Cruz, show us what you got."

Johnny had some distinct advantages over me in this ride. He was familiar with the route, had won the previous year, and he had the right gear, including a snug Lycra shirt, form-fitted Lycra riding shorts, and cleated shoes for improved upstroke power. Johnny was no slouch. He trained year-round; ski-racing in the winter and mountain biking all summer.

However, I was also was in great shape. My daily rides up the Bells made this flat terrain feel like nothing, and Aikido helped my breathing stay relaxed and even in tempo. However, there is an art to racing a time trial.

Delatori interrupted, "What do you mean 'art' to racing a time trial?" he asked.

Manual nodded and said, "The time trial isn't just about speed and power, it's about becoming narrow and aerodynamic. Tour de

France greats like Greg LeMond had an uncanny ability to make themselves small. LeMond once made up fifty seconds on Laurent Fignon to win the 1989 Tour de France by only eight seconds, capping off the closest Tour finish in history. LeMond won mainly because of his narrow position on the bike, something that at that point in my life, I was not used to."

"So, you weren't 'artful' that day?" Delatori teased.

"No, Van Gogh, I was not. That level of technique takes a tremendous amount of practice. But I do remember something else about that day that was off."

Delatori urged Manuel to continue.

There was something wrong, but I couldn't figure out what it was. The bike didn't seem to glide like it normally did. I was putting a tremendous amount of force through each pedal stroke to maintain my speed yet struggled to keep up my rpms.

As I passed a popular camping spot called Difficult Campground, I looked up to see Johnny descending towards me in a unique position. He was teetering on the front lip of his saddle and his chin was so low it almost touched the stem. His elbows were tucked in tight, and his knees pinched the top tube of the bike. I had never seen this position before, but I liked it and made a mental note for my descent. As I approached the gate, there was some of the strangest music I had ever heard blaring down the pass. A psychedelic keyboard riff, thunderous drums and trippy lyrics blared from the back of Coach's truck. "Strange Days," to pure Doors fans, is a brilliant and iconic song. However, to a recently transplanted Mexican immigrant hearing it for the first time, it was disorienting and aptly named.

I reached the gate. Both Coach and Paul were cheering wildly. "Stay strong and keep it tight on the descent. You're twenty-two seconds off pace and have to make up some time!"

"How can I be twenty-two seconds behind? I have been riding like a man possessed," I thought to myself. On the ride back, everything seemed magnified as Coach's voice echoed in my head. "You're twenty-two seconds behind, you're twenty-two seconds behind." On my descent from Independence Pass, I became distracted by the passing cars, swallowed a bug (which seemed to get stuck halfway down my esophagus) and felt every bump in the road. The demon image I had conjured up of my parents being murdered was fleeting as I struggled to focus. I tried to remember the descending position that Johnny employed, but couldn't remember if his hands were in the drops or tucked tightly towards the stem. I had been "red-lining" for over twenty minutes now, my quads felt like they were on the verge of cramping and my vision became hazy. It was official—I was bonking.

"Bonking? What the heck is that?" Delatori interrupted.

"You're not familiar with bonking, my friend?" Manuel responded.

Delatori jiggled his beer belly with both hands until it shook like Jell-O, and said with a regretful smile, "Sorry, Manuel, my athletic days are in the rearview mirror."

"Well, let me tell you about the bonk in lay terms." Manuel said with an enthusiastic tone. "Imagine a tightly-wrapped ace bandage placed around your torso so that you can't expand your ribs for a deep inhalation. Then a hot, wet rag is placed around your face, covering your nose and mouth. A set of confining horse blinders is then placed on you, so your gaze is limited and imprisoning. Then imagine you are forced to sprint up fifty flights of stairs to avoid a fire. You hit the thirtieth floor and your mind, with clarity and focus, tells your body to continue fleeing. But your musculoskeletal system responds by saying, 'I have actually lived long enough. I think I am going to just lay down next to this cozy fireplace and sleep.' That, my friend, is the bonk, and on my way

back through Aspen heading towards the high school that day, I had a one-way ticket to Bonkville."

Manuel continued, "There have been many epic failures in sports. Lindsey Jacobellis was close to winning the gold medal in the 2006 Winter Games in snowboard cross when she fell while showing off on one of the final jumps. Then there was Iron Mike Tyson getting knocked out in the tenth round to little-known Buster Douglas (a 42-1 underdog). It's also hard to forget the Seattle Seahawks who, in Super Bowl XLIX with the ball on the one-yard-line, three downs remaining, and arguably the best running back in the league, Marshawn Lynch, tried to throw a pass that was intercepted by Malcolm Butler, giving New England a last-second win. Well, the choke I was experiencing was right up there. By the time I got back to the high school parking lot, I was listless and despondent. I had fallen from twenty-two seconds back to 2:44 off Johnny's pace."

"Gather 'round, guys." said Coach Carmouche as we all huddled up in the high school parking lot. I dragged my carcass towards Coach and with blurred vision tried to focus on his silhouette. "I am truly proud of all of you. You put your hearts on the line today, and you all performed like champions. Special congratulations to Johnny with the fastest time of the day and Stretch with the second-best time. These are our guys this year. Rally around them and let's go dominate!"

Coach came over to me as I slumped on a bench, eyes glazed, head in my hands and barely coherent. He put his arm around my shoulder and said, "Great work out there, Cruz. That was an inspired performance, and it shows you have the heart of a champion. You will live to ride another day."

Delatori raised his eyebrows inquisitively, "What do you think happened? You rode so well only two days prior?"

"Would you believe that my good friend, Johnny, had something to do with it?" Manuel responded sardonically.

18

GWAI LO

"I will be back."

—Andy Schleck, winner of the 2010 Tour de France

"The rest of that week I was depleted and had abandoned the dream of becoming a bike racer for the school of Aspen," Manuel explained. "I had really expected to win and thought that maybe I wasn't as good as everyone else thought? I even investigated the Debate Club."

"I thought you had no interest in debate," said Delatori.

"Exactly. But I figured maybe I needed to practice and get better. I also liked the fact that through thoughtful and concise rhetoric, one could deflect, redirect and resolve conflict the way Chief Akecheta did in political science class," Manuel explained.

"Not to spoil your story, Manuel, but I am pretty confident your biking days weren't over." announced Delatori.

"You are correct, sir." replied Manuel. "Coach Carmouche had been waiting for me to return to practice all week to discuss the time trial. When I failed to attend practice, he went to the one place he knew I would be: Aikido. Coach waited patiently outside the dojo for me to finish class."

"Hey, Cruz, everyone's been asking about you, where you been?" asked Coach Carmouche. Tom listened from behind a rice paper screen.

"I'm just not cut out for that stuff, Coach. You saw. You were there," I said.

"Cruz, did you notice something wrong with your bike during the time trial?" asked Coach.

"Yeah, I did notice something wrong. Its driver wasn't fast enough," I replied sarcastically.

"Cruz, my assistant was checking out your bike after the time trial to see how you had it set up and noticed your rear rim was gently brushing up against the rear brake: you basically were riding against your brake for the entire time trial. To be completely honest, you have more raw talent than anyone I have ever coached in my career. You need to come back and train with us." pleaded Coach Carmouche.

"The team hates me. They think I am Mexican trash." I countered.

"The team doesn't hate you. Okay, maybe Johnny does, but that's because you're better than him. In fact, I have a suspicion he was the one that messed with your rear brake. Listen, I have a good friend, Riggs Kearny, who runs a testing facility out of the Aspen Club. I want you to come by to take a VO2 max stress test. If you perform well, I might be able to make you one of the top riders on the team. Nationals are in six weeks, Cruz, and we could use your help. This could eventually get you a scholarship to a Division I school and change your life forever. Please, just think about it." Coach said as he put his hand on my shoulder before exiting the dojo.

Confused and distraught, I went back towards Tom's office. Tom, who was pretending to manicure a bonsai tree, greeted me with a sympathetic smile.

"Did you hear all that, Tom?" I asked.

"Hear what? The fact that you have more raw talent than Coach Carmouche has ever seen? Nope, didn't hear a thing!"

"Why should I race for a team that hates and sabotages me?" I argued.

"Why do you think they hate you?" asked Sensei.

"I don't know. I guess because I am different. People who look like me in this valley are gardeners and house cleaners and don't hang out with the white kids." I snorted in anger.

Sensei stayed calm and listened, "Come here, I want to show you something." Tom led me to a dimly-lit back room with katana swords and a large framed picture of Bruce Lee on the wall. "Did you know that when Bruce Lee came to America he was an outcast? Not just among whites, but even among Asian Americans," commented Tom.

I was puzzled. "I thought Bruce Lee was a hero and loved by everyone."

"No, Cruz, not early on. There was a code within the Cantonese community that the Cantonese masters, like Bruce Lee, were forbidden to teach martial arts to the 'Gwai Lo'—Caucasian Americans. But you see, Bruce was a revolutionary. He truly believed if he could share the Cantonese culture, including martial arts, with mainstream America, he could break down barriers, build rapport and change the bilateral hatred and discrimination endemic between eastern and western cultures.

In fact, the Cantonese leadership was so furious with Bruce teaching whites that they threatened if he continued to teach the Gwai Lo, he would have to fight the most feared and deadly martial artist in San Francisco, Wong Jack Man. Wong

Jack Man was known for his deadly power, surgical accuracy, and most importantly, his undefeated street fighting record. If Bruce won the fight, he would be allowed to continue his quest of disseminating knowledge to the Gwai Lo. If he lost, he would be exiled from the community. These were the highest of stakes, but facing injury and alienation from his own people, Bruce followed his heart and elected to fight for what he believed was righteous and just."

"Did he win?" I asked.

"Of course, he won. He was Bruce Lee! Cruz, they are scared of you. Show them who you are. Share your spirit with them. Share your work ethic with them. Share your culture with them. Don't let them get to you." Tom responded. "Cruz, you are not only a gifted athlete, you have a superior will and intellect. Don't let them, or anyone else, stop you on your quest towards self-actualization."

"Sensei, you are the BEST!" I said, as I embraced Tom in a hug.

"No, Cruz, Bruce Lee is the best. I am just Tom."

19

ASPEN HIGH

"Give a man a fish and feed him for a day. Teach a man to fish and feed him for a lifetime. Teach a man to cycle and he will realize fishing is stupid and boring."

—Desmond Tutu,
South African theologian and human rights activist

Friday morning, in political science class, Chief Akecheta talked about legendary philosopher Immanuel Kant's ethical constructs as they applied to the African American civil rights activist, Rosa Parks. We had been studying this era in American politics and we'd learned about her amazing act of defiance in refusing to give up her seat on a bus to a white person, and how her case eventually became an instrumental step in the U.S. Supreme Court passing the Civil Rights Act of 1964.

"Did the bus driver have a categorical imperative to kick Rosa Parks from her seat?" asked Chief Akecheta. Simultaneously, Summer whispered to me, "Do you want to go to a party tonight at Difficult Campground?"

"YES!" I quickly replied in a loud voice.

"Yes?" Chief Akecheta questioned. "The bus driver did have a categorical imperative to kick Rosa Parks off the bus?"

"I mean, um … no?" I responded, fumbling over my words.

"Well, which one is it, Mr. Delgado? Yes or no?"

"No, sir," I replied, as Summer snickered under her breath.

I couldn't tell if Summer actually liked me, or if she was just feeling badly after seeing the way Johnny treated me. Later that night, I got on my bike and made my way east towards Independence Pass en route to Difficult Campground. I arrived at an impressive scene. Two raging bonfires kicked up ten-foot flames, illuminating the entire west side of the campground. Chuckie cooked up brats and burgers on a massive grill, and a boom box was pumping out tunes.

The ambiguity of Summer's invitation swirled around in my head. I knew that Summer and Johnny had a history together, but I had never seen them holding hands or kissing. My brain began flip-flopping around like a ball caroming around a roulette wheel. "What if she was just inviting me as a friend?

Why would she invite me as a friend, she has plenty of friends already? Doesn't she hate immigrants like her father? Just because she is Mr. Campbell's daughter, doesn't mean she shares his political views. What if Johnny gets even more irritated with me than he already is? I'm not scared of Johnny, he is the one that should be scared of me," I thought to myself as I showed up on The Red Rocket 2.0 wearing khaki slacks, a red and black long-sleeved flannel shirt, and some brown Timberland boots I borrowed from Domi.

As I approached the bonfire, I could hear Robert Palmer's "Addicted to Love" pounding out from the boom box, I saw girls dancing together holding hands and dudes chugging beer. "Man," I thought to myself, "You're not in Tizayuca anymore."

Summer snuck up from behind me and grabbed me by the arm, "Come here. I want to ask you something." She pulled me away from the group until we were out of earshot of any of the other kids. "The other day when Johnny attacked you. How did you—I mean—you didn't even have a scratch on you." Summer stammered over her words as she gazed into my eyes.

"It's called Aikido. It's all about flowing like water." I gently grabbed Summer's wrists with both hands. "Put your right foot back in a fighting stance … bend your knees … now simply trace my movement." I began to oscillate our arms in a smooth elliptical motion. I then made the motion larger and more aggressive. "Flow with your opponent's energy, just like a tall willow tree bends with the wind, but never breaks." I slowly circled to my left. Summer followed as we continued to match ellipses with our arms. "So often, we meet force with force. The beauty of Aikido is in redirecting force, deflating conflict, unifying energy," I said.

"Well, look what we have here. What's up, vato?" Johnny said popping up from behind us with Chuckie in tow.

"Hey, Johnny, congratulations on the time trial," I replied.

"Yeah, imagine how good it must feel to be the number one rider on the best team in the state. Let's celebrate, Johnny bellowed. Chuckie, load me up!" Chuckie proceeded to set up a long funnel connected to a one-inch hose.

"What the heck is that?" I asked Summer.

"It's a beer bong."

"A beer bong?" I replied inquisitively.

"Just watch, Cruz." Summer stated as Chuckie handed the hose to Johnny.

"JOHNNY ... JOHNNY ... JOHNNY" the crowd clamored as Johnny downed the beer and let out a triumphant "BUUUUUURP!"

"Your turn, Cruz," said Johnny.

I glanced reluctantly at Summer. She tilted her head slightly to the right and smiled as if to say, "Why not?"

"You realize you are on the record, Mr. Delgado," Delatori interrupted, chuckling.

The senate hopeful smiled wryly, "Ha, ha; yes, I know. I am all about full disclosure on this campaign, and this will be a great lesson for all the youngsters out there why they should NEVER do this."

"Oh, boy," Delatori said. "I can only assume things didn't end well."

"You are correct, sir, they didn't." Manuel replied.

"So, I grabbed the beer bong with authority, positioned myself below Chuckie in an athletic stance and said, "Vámanos!" The problem was that while Chuckie was pouring beer in the funnel, Johnny, who was just out of my visual field, was also pouring in vodka."

"CRUZ ... CRUZ ... CRUZ," the crowd cheered, as I finished the entire funnel. I put the tube down and began to stagger backwards. My stagger turned into a free fall, and I ended up crashing into some brush on the edge of the campsite as the crowd erupted in laughter.

Summer, having seen what Johnny did, went over and slapped his arm. "You're such an asshole," she said.

"It's a gift." Johnny replied.

"Wait a minute, had you ever consumed alcohol before this point?" asked Delatori.

"Not really," replied Manuel. "My only experience with it was on my thirteenth birthday. Pops had brought me out to the backyard in Tizayuca. 'Son, this is an important day in your life.' he said. 'You are no longer a boy. You are a young man, full of responsibility, strength and courage and although I am not a big drinker, nor do I condone alcohol, it's time for your first drink.' Then he popped the cap off an ice-cold Tecate from the cooler.

"That week in Tizayuca, a heat wave had rolled in. Even though I didn't much like the taste of the beer, there was something about the fizziness, the aftertaste and the ice-cold temperature that satisfied me. I will never forget that moment I shared bonding with Pops, the taste of a cold beer on a hot summer day, and the feeling

of respect I received as I grew into a young man; certainly not the experience I had that night at the Difficult Campground party."

I tried to get up but stumbled again. I looked at Summer, and the machismo I had prior to downing the beer bong was replaced with embarrassment and humiliation. A visceral discomfort travelled from my stomach up into my throat and I sensed I was about to vomit. I staggered over to my bike as Summer watched disappointedly. "I gotta get out of here before I embarrass myself anymore," I slurred, as I mounted my bike.

My ride home was more than interesting. The east end of Aspen is lit only by the stars and moon and can be eerily dark at night. Thankfully, on this particular night, the moon was waxing and the roads were illuminated, which gave me some bearing on the road. I stopped frequently to shake the "drunk" out of my head, and on one stop even plunged my face into the ice-cold Roaring Fork river to try and stop the mountains from spinning around me. I finally made it home, stumbled into my bedroom and plunged down on the plush comforter, laying comatose until late the next morning.

20

TO THE MAX

"Pain is still the friend that always tells me the truth."

—Chris Froome, British road racing cyclist and winner of the 2018 Giro d'Italia

I woke up Saturday morning feeling like death. My head pounded, the room spun, and I slept for most of the morning. I couldn't understand how my uncle—or anyone for that matter—would choose to feel like this on a regular basis. My thoughts drifted to what Coach Carmouche had said a couple days earlier. "You have more raw talent than anyone I have ever coached … this could get you a scholarship to a Division I college."

I went outside to the storage shed that housed The Red Rocket and sat down across from it. The sun shone in from a window to the east and hit the front sprocket spraying rays of light like a prism across the walls of the shed. "What a beautiful invention," I thought, "a simple mechanical vehicle, that doesn't require gas, requires minimal servicing and can take you anywhere you want to go." At that moment, I knew where I wanted to go and that The Red Rocket would help take me there. I rested most the day, alternating between my bed and the couch and back to my bed again. My head stopped pounding and finally, after a big meal of scrambled eggs and pancakes, I decided to reach out to Coach Carmouche to schedule the VO2 max test.

Domi had told me about the legendary Aspen Club. "You won't believe this place Manny. It's as prestigious a sports complex as they come. I used to help a friend with maintenance there and would see sports legends like Tennis Hall of Famer Martina Navratilova, two-time World Series MVP Reggie Jackson, and skiing legend Klaus Obermeyer. The cool thing for you, Manny, is that although the club is frequented by multisport athletes, its niche is road cyclists.

I showed up on Sunday afternoon to the legendary Aspen Club. I worked my way past the reception desk, towards an overlook which gave view to a 5,000-square-foot exercise facility on the first floor below. I stood in shock, gazing down towards the first level of the gym, which opened up to a seventy-foot-high ceiling. I had once seen a postcard of the Disneyland theme park in California that highlighted spectacular rides, brightly-colored architecture, and kids smiling from ear-to-ear. This place looked like Disneyland for fitness enthusiasts. Looking down on the space, attractive and uber-fit locals threw medicine balls, moved free weights and guided machines up and down. Shaking my head in disbelief, I looked up towards the heavens, "Pops, you would have loved it here," I thought to myself. The second floor that circled the gym from above was equipped with cardiovascular equipment, a Pilates studio, a cafe, a Physical Therapy clinic and the legendary Carmouche High Altitude Testing Facility, where I was to take the VO2 test.

"Excuse me, Manuel, what is the VO2 test again? Delatori asked. "I feel like I read about it once in a Wall Street Journal article dealing with fitness testing, but it was some time ago."

"The VO2 max test is a measurement of the rate of oxygen used during incrementally progressive exercise." exclaimed Manuel.

"Um, in English for my readers?" quipped Delatori.

"Right," Manuel replied with a sympathetic smile. "It is basically one's aerobic fitness level; the higher the score, the better you are at prolonged aerobic events like cycling.

The challenge comes in taking the test. It is revealing, humbling and exhausting. Any flaw in technique, any weakness in the supporting muscle groups and any lapse in previous training shows up in spades for everyone to see."

"My man, you made it," said Coach Carmouche. "I would like you to meet Dr. Riggs Kearny, who will be running the test and assessing the final numbers. How're you feeling today, Stallion?" asked Coach.

"Pretty darn good," I answered.

"Well, let's rock and roll," said Riggs, who loved nothing more than testing high-level athletes.

Riggs began to adjust the bike for me. He elevated the stem, dropped the seat back and adjusted the handlebars to my liking. He also began entering information into the computer: age, weight, body fat measurements, blood pressure, resting pulse. "Coach, check this out—this kid's resting pulse is 43!" Riggs said, with a large grin on his face.

"Yes, sir, just wait till he gets going," replied Coach Carmouche.

"Cruz, the test starts out at 100 watts for four minutes and goes up fifty watts every four minutes thereafter. After you complete the 250-watt stage, the resistance jumps thirty-five watts every two minutes, until you fail," Riggs instructed.

"I won't fail," I retorted.

"Everyone fails," interjected Coach. Both Coach and Riggs snickered over my machismo.

Riggs proceeded to place a face mask on me that fastened with elastic straps on the back of my head.

"What's this?" I asked, in a muffled voice.

"The mask only allows contained air to pass into the lungs. I know it's uncomfortable and can feel a little claustrophobic, but you should adjust after a few minutes," replied Riggs.

At first, I was thrown off by the bulky and restrictive mask. However, I remembered what Coach said about "finding your demon." I thought back to the nightmare my family had to endure on the way to the border. The unsaturated oxygen levels in the back of the truck had made breathing laborious and taxing. I remembered the air being so thick, that I literally had to "gulp" it in, like a fish trying to survive out of water. Being folded into the crate didn't help matters. My rib cage had been compressed down towards my pelvis, placing tremendous pressure on my diaphragm and accessory breathing muscles. I vividly remembered my parents' wispy and strained breathing and could even hear others struggling for air from surrounding crates … demon conjured!

"This VO2 test is NOTHING," I thought silently to myself, as I sat atop the bike with the mask firmly secured in place.

The test began and was fairly simple in the earlier stages. I was literally "CRUZing!" Keeping my rpms around eighty, I hit the 390-watt stage without too much difficulty. Both coaches looked at one another with relative surprise, as this stage represented an approximate VO2 of 60.0, a strong result for highly trained adult men. However, I was not done, not by a long shot. I went to 425 watts, then to 460 watts.

"This kid's heart is going to explode," said Riggs. "It's been over 195 for more than ten minutes!"

"He's okay," replied Coach Carmouche, "I have seen this before. Let him go." Lactic acid was now coursing through my legs, my lungs burned and even my arms were tired from holding position, but I continued driving the pedals towards the floor with explosive consistency.

"Holy smokes," bellowed Riggs. "How old is this kid?"

"He's seventeen," answered Coach Carmouche.

"Well, your seventeen-year-old just hit 495 watts. That's better than some of my pro riders."

Sweat was gushing out of every pore of my body, and my accessory breathing muscles around my rib cage, chest and neck started to seize up. My heart rate, which was now 204, hadn't changed for several minutes. My knees began to flare in trying to steal any type of mechanical advantage I could get and my head began to bob side-to-side with every crank of the pedals. I felt like a rag doll.

"Shut him down," ordered Coach.

With rabid excitement over what he had just seen, Riggs frantically began running numbers on the computer, while Coach Carmouche peeled off my mask. I collapsed on the floor in the corner of the room as Coach sprayed ice-cold water from a bottle on my torso and began fanning me with a large towel. I writhed on the floor, trying to find a position of comfort. My lungs ached, and my legs were "en fuego!" I rolled from my right side to my left, flexing and extending my legs, and rotated my hips in and out searching for some relief.

"Where we at, Riggs?" asked Coach Carmouche with eager anticipation.

"This can't be right," said Riggs. "There's no way this kid pulled a VO2 of seventy-three at this altitude. That would put him at around an eighty at sea level!"

"Don't forget, Cruz grew up cycling in the high-altitude mountains of Mexico. He has more hemoglobin in his blood than a mountain goat. Double-check your numbers," barked Coach Carmouche.

"I still can't believe it, but this is right … adjusted for altitude, this kid has the VO2 max of some of my top-level professional racers!" said Riggs.

Coach Carmouche looked at Riggs with an animated, testosterone-fueled stare: "I told you, man, this kid is a FREAK!"

Then he turned toward me, "Congratulations, Cruz. You just earned your spot as an A-List rider on our team."

I looked up from my jellyfish-like position on the floor. With mouth gaping and eyes half-mast, I gave Coach a thumbs-up and whispered in a weary voice, "Viva Mexico!"

21

PUNCH BOWL

"To me, it doesn't matter whether it's raining or the sun is shining or whatever: as long as I am riding a bike I know I am the luckiest guy in the world."

—Mark Cavendish, world champion track cyclist

I was on cloud nine after my epic V02 test and returned to school on Monday with a new-found confidence. My teammates had heard about my performance at the Aspen Club and as they passed me in the hall, they offered up comments like, "Here comes Super-Cruz," and "What's up, freak?" One guy joked as he walked past me and said, "Where's your next race, the Kentucky Derby?" Even Johnny chimed in, "I guess all the rice and beans finally paid off."

I loved the accolades, but more importantly, I felt like I was part of the team. Summer must have also been impressed.

"A bunch of us are riding mountain bikes to the Punch Bowl tomorrow. You should come," she said.

"Punch Bowl?" I asked.

"Yeah, it's pretty cool. You can jump off a big ledge into super-deep water," said Summer.

"It would have to be after bike practice," I replied.

"I thought superstars didn't have to practice," she said, as she smiled and flipped her hair flirtatiously over her shoulder. "I'll pick you up after practice," she instructed, as she walked off.

I was beaming and floated through school the rest of the day.

The next day, Summer drove me up to a trailhead a few miles below the Punch Bowl in her convertible Saab. The usual suspects from the cycling team were there, including Johnny, his friend, Chuckie, and another dozen girls and guys from the high school. The trailhead parking lot was a frenzy of activity. I heard Carlos Santana's "Hope You're Feeling Better" blasting from Johnny's car stereo as we pulled in. "Maybe this guy had some redeeming qualities after all," I thought to myself. I recognized Santana's music right away because Domi listened to his songs incessantly on the local KSPN radio station and had a tradition of yelling out "CARLOOOOOSSSSS" the instant one of his songs would come on. Not wanting Summer to think I was too weird, but also not wanting to let Domi down, I quietly muttered, "Carloooooosssss!"

As we pulled in, Ken was riding a wheelie straight toward us and had to quickly veer off path to avoid hitting Summer's car. Stretch bunny-hopped his bike onto the front hood of his Dodge Dart and proceeded to ride smoothly over the roof, popping a wheelie off the trunk and landing on his rear wheel as he came off the back of the vehicle. I had never seen riding like this before. I was in awe of these guys.

The midday sun crested high above the Rockies and the smell of fresh pine filled the air. Chuckie proceeded to chug a bottle of Gatorade. Stopping short of finishing the bottle, he poured the rest onto his head, shook his head from side to side like a wet dog coming out of a bath, and hollered, "Let's ride!"

Our group ripped through the single track like a pack of hungry wolves. We jumped over stumps, splashed through creek beds and flew off ledges on our way to the famous Punch Bowl. I was surprised to see Summer's proficiency on a bike. She rode with grace, fluidity and stamina. I had never been a part of such an athletic group of individuals; it was empowering. After fifteen minutes of riding, the densely-wooded path cleared into an open space filled with tall field grass and sparse boulders.

"Is this place for real?" I yelled up towards Summer.

"Wait 'til you see the Punch Bowl!" she hollered back.

We approached a bluff that was comprised entirely of rock. The pack proceeded to lay their bikes down and sprawl out on the rock face. I set my bike down, grabbed some water and began to clean my sunglasses off with the bottom of my shirt. Through the reflection in my glasses, I saw Summer taking off her riding shirt, revealing a baby blue string top bikini and gently-toned abdominals. "What is this, a beer commercial?" I thought in disbelief.

Summer turned towards me, "Are you coming?" she asked.

As we began to ascend the slab rock, she taught me about the area. "The Punch Bowl was carved out by the Roaring Fork River," she said. "The rock formation has three tiers. The first one hovers ten feet above the river and is where we all laid our bikes. The second ledge is about thirty feet above the water but is only accessible from the north side. The third tier is about fifty feet above the water's surface. That's the one we're going to."

"Fifty feet," I gulped. "Isn't that a little dangerous?"

"It can be." she replied. "You don't want to jump during spring runoff, as the current is too strong and has been known to pull people under. But it's fine now."

She led me up a slab rock path that had small pine trees growing in it.

"How do these trees grow out of the rock?" I asked.

"It's Aspen, Cruz. Anything is possible here." Summer replied as she turned flirtatiously back towards me.

We made our way to the summit. Summer took my hand and said, "Let's sit down and take this in."

We sat and listened to the water as it crashed over the rocks below. As the sun warmed our shoulders, we noticed two chipmunks playfully chasing one another up a tree. I exhaled deeply and for the first time since I had arrived in Aspen, I experienced a sense of complete calm.

"So, I hear you're quite the phenom on a bike," said Summer.

"My parents got me a bike for my thirteenth birthday. We were very poor at the time, but they sacrificed for me. They wanted me to ride in the mountains after school, to avoid interacting with the drug gangs."

"Drug gangs? Are you serious?" Summer asked.

"Yeah, it was crazy. They would try to recruit the neighborhood kids into their gang. Once you were in, you could never leave. I didn't use the bike for exercise, it was a way to escape. I guess it became a symbol of my freedom. When I am on a bike, I feel like my life is going somewhere, like I'm moving forward. I guess it's in my blood now."

"Then why did you almost quit after the time trials?" she continued.

"That was rough," I replied. "Biking is such a part of me that I felt like a failure when I didn't perform well. And being that I am ..." I paused.

"Being what?" Summer asked.

I slowly looked into Summer's eyes. "Being Mexican; I feel like an outsider. Don't get me wrong, Summer. I love my people and my heritage. It's just so different here. I thought being a top cyclist on the Aspen team would help me fit in." I replied. "When I didn't do well at the time trial, it stopped me in my tracks."

"I work with many young kids in the *Finding Your Groove* program that would be eternally grateful to ride like you and have the opportunities you have, Cruz. You are intelligent, thoughtful and have more potential than I think you realize. And furthermore, your heritage has given you an amazing tan," Summer said jokingly.

I stared deeply into her eyes. Her words comforted me but also challenged me to be more grateful for my place in the universe.

Suddenly, she reached toward me. "What's that?" she asked as she gently lifted the cross pendant from my chest.

"It's my mom's necklace. She gave it to me before she ..." I paused. "Before we came to America," I said.

"It's beautiful," Summer replied.

A flash of heat surged through my body, tightening my chest and making me flush. The sun cast a glow on Summer's face, highlighting small freckles and other tiny imperfections that can only be seen when two people are sitting face-to-face. Was this really happening? Was I about to kiss the most popular and attractive girl at Aspen High School? I gently folded my hand atop hers. Her palm was silky and smooth, and I could feel its warmth. I nervously leaned in to kiss her, and just then, from the first tier, fifty feet below, Chuckie, who always had exquisite timing, hollered, "Jump, you pussies!"

Startled, I pulled away and we both scrambled to our feet. I looked out over the edge of the fifty-foot drop and froze. "Oh, Dios mío!"

"What? Is the superhero scared of heights?" Summer asked.

"Yes! Yes! There's two things I don't like, cold water and heights, and I am pretty confident both of those things are present right now."

"We got this," Summer said, as she forcibly grabbed my hand.

"You trust me, right?" she asked. I nodded. "Okay, take a deep breath, tighten your core and keep your arms close to your sides."

"ONE ... TWO ... THREE!" Summer counted.

I closed my eyes, and although I had not been happy with God in recent times, I kissed Mama's necklace, pushed off the lip of the slab rock and prayed to Jesus the whole way down.

KERSPLOUSH! We were greeted by the crisp, frigid water of the Roaring Fork. Torpedoing downward towards the riverbed, I remember being surprised to never feel my feet hit the bottom.

"WHOO-HOO," I hollered upon emerging from the depths of the icy water. Summer nodded towards a shallow pool of slow-moving water just below the entry point of the Punch Bowl. "Follow me." she said, as we quickly swam towards the shore.

Coming out of the deep waters of the Punch Bowl, we finally felt some loose gravel beneath our feet, and both rose from the water covered in goosebumps. Dipping back under the water, Summer tilted her head back to clear her hair from her face and slowly emerged into my gaze. Her aqua blue eyes pierced through me with sharp definition and assurance. She grabbed the front edge of my board shorts and slowly pulled me towards her. Shivering, I placed both hands gently on the side of her cheeks, pulled her head towards mine and gently met her lips, tasting her for the first time. The kiss was soft, sensual and everything I thought a first kiss would be. Summer gently pulled away from me after several seconds. A tear had pooled under my left eye and then raced down the side of my face. "Are you okay?" she asked.

"Never better," I answered through quivering lips.

Since the passing of my mother, I had questioned if I would ever have another woman in my life that would look at me the way my mother did—a woman who would fawn over me, respect me, embrace me, love me. Summer was the most exquisite woman I had ever met and being in her presence made me feel whole again.

22

GO TIME

"Cycling isn't a game, it's a sport. Tough, hard and unpitying, it requires great sacrifices. One plays football, or tennis or hockey. One does not play cycling."

—Jean de Gribaldy:
French road cyclist and director of Sportif

"Mark, look outside and tell me what you see," Manuel said as he took a big swig of FIJI water. Both men got up out of their chairs and looked out the plate glass window onto Confluence Park.

"Well, I see some sunbathers, a couple kayakers and a heck of a lot of bicyclists," remarked Delatori.

"You're darn right. There are a heck of a lot of bicyclists out there, because this is a biking state. Some states like Florida and Texas are known for football. Other states like New York and Chi-

cago are basketball states, but not Colorado. Colorado is known for cycling, and the state high school road cycling program has historically produced some of the best cyclists in the nation. The high school cycling season in Colorado is short in duration yet has a profound impact on the young individuals involved," Manuel commented.

"So, tell me about the season. Is there a state championship?" asked Delatori.

"There isn't a state championship per se, but teams compete for point totals. At the end of the season, the two top finishing teams go on to compete at Nationals. Nationals is a big deal because kids get selected for the U.S. Junior Olympic team, and also get recruited by prominent colleges. That first year I attended Aspen High, our schedule had the Aspen Rebels traveling to Steamboat to open the season, followed by Telluride, Summit County, back to Aspen, I think we then traveled to Golden, Montrose and finished in Vail. Although historically Vail was the biggest adversary to the Rebels, Montrose had been producing top riders back then and was emerging as one of the stronger cycling communities in the nation," Manuel explained. "Let me tell you about my first race. It was a doozy!"

My maiden voyage into the world of competitive cycling would be no cake walk. As our team headed north towards Steamboat on U.S. 40 over Rabbit Ears Pass, we noticed ominous storm clouds beginning to form. From Kremmling, looking west to Hayden, east towards Sheep Mountain and north to Routt National Forest, cumulonimbus storm clouds danced, thundered, and roared overhead, creating a mosaic of evil in the late day sky. As we got closer to Steamboat, the clouds went from grey to black and began to spit crooked daggers of light throughout the valley. For someone who had never witnessed an electrical storm like this before, I deduced that God was sending a message to all riders that "today is not your day to race. These are my mountains, and I will dictate who will have safe trespass on them." For the first time in my cycling experience, I had genuine fear and trepidation about riding.

The team arrived and began to prepare for the race. Coach distributed rain gear, Gatorade and power bars.

"Isn't this awesome, gentlemen? It's our first race of the season, and we are blessed with this kind of an opportunity; an opportunity to band together, an opportunity to overcome adversity, an opportunity to test our mettle and an opportunity to deliver the first win of our undefeated season." stated Coach.

"Undefeated?" Bobby asked.

"You heard me," replied Coach. "Look around, gentlemen. What do you see? I'll tell you what I see—potential. I have been coaching this team for over a decade; I have won three national titles, produced two Olympians, never had a losing season, and have yet to assemble a stronger team than what you see before you. We are not only going to win today, we will dominate every aspect of this race from start to finish, and this is how we are going to do it.

Step one—intimidation. I want all the team to publicly speak of our new addition, Cruz Delgado. Talk about him like he is legend. Mention his recent 73 VO2 max test, tell the other teams that your coach thinks he is the best high school cyclist in the nation.

Step two—charge. Cruz, after twenty-five kilometers, you, Ben and Zeth are going to lead an early breakaway riding like your hair's on fire; all the other top teams will counter. Johnny, Bobby, Kevin and Paul are going to stay back with the peloton, conserving energy.

Step three—reel them in. With twenty kilometers to go and fresh legs, Johnny, you and your pod will separate from the main peloton, reel in the breakaway group and Team Aspen will place 1-2-3, securing our first win of the season."

Johnny, excited to know he was still the number one rider exclaimed, "Let's do this!"

"Bring it in, guys." The team all put their right hands on top of Coach's.

Coach yelled, "INJECT," and the team responded, "VEN-OM!"

Coach yelled out again with increased intensity, "INJECT!"

"VENOM!" we yelled back.

The third time Coach yelled "INJECT" we threw our fists in the air, summoning the gods of cycling and screamed, "VENOM!"

Coach Carmouche had come up with the "Venom" motto years earlier, after he suspected a Vail coach of purposefully having one of his riders instigate a crash, putting a top-tier Team Aspen rider in the hospital. Coach Carmouche, although a great sportsman, was an equally fierce competitor. Coach didn't just want to win events, he wanted to inject venom into his opponents, rendering them disoriented, helpless, dejected, and on the losing end of every race against the Rebels.

As the riders gathered at the starting point, I could overhear some of the team talking me up. Johnny said to Brian Davis, team captain for Vail, "Check out our new phenom. This kid doesn't feel pain. He has only one speed—warp!"

Bobby coasted over to Scott Eggert from Montrose; "Have you seen our new stud? He just pulled a 73 VO2 max at altitude. You guys are screwed."

"That's bullshit. Your coach probably couldn't even pull a 73," Scott rebutted.

“Seriously, the kid grew up riding in the mountains of Mexico. He has more hemoglobin than GOD.” Bobby replied.

Within minutes, every team was plotting on how to keep me in their sights.

BANG!

The gunshot rang through the late afternoon air, signaling the start of the race. The roads were saturated with rain, which brought oil and antifreeze tailings to the top of the concrete. The peloton drudged slowly through the rain, wind and cold. I was so frigid my legs went numb. “At least I won’t feel any pain,” I thought to myself.

The rain intensified, weighing riders down, impeding vision and making road conditions treacherous. However, it was the lightning that concerned me the most. A week earlier, in the *Aspen Times* newspaper, there was a report of a family being struck by lightning as they slept in their tent at the Lost Man Loop Campground. One of the family members even died. I couldn’t seem to shake the image from my head.

The peloton was only fifteen kilometers into the race, but I had warmed up and didn’t understand this slow pace, plus I wanted to get this thing over with and get away from the lightning. “Close enough,” I barked to my teammates. “Vámonos, vámanos,” I yelled. Ben and Zeth—looking confused, as we weren’t supposed to attack until twenty-five kilometers in—got off their saddles and reluctantly followed me as we jumped out in front of the peloton.

"Shit," I heard a rider from Montrose bark out as Zeth, Ben and I whizzed past. The majority of riders were not warm yet, but just like Coach had anticipated, the top riders from Vail, Montrose, Steamboat and Summit County followed the attack.

I vaulted out to a blistering pace of 98 rpms as our breakaway accelerated on the undulating terrain. Ben, Zeth and I took turns leading the breakaway pack, with me taking the longest lead times out front. The other teams followed with strong performances from their top riders. On one of my rest cycles, one of the riders from Vail, rode up on my left. "Hace buen tiempo," I said, flashing him a smile.

"What?" shouted the Vail rider.

"Nice weather we are having," I exclaimed as rain continued to pour from the sky. The Vail rider looked at me like I was crazy, bowed his head down and continued to hammer.

I was now thoroughly warmed up and felt strong, determined and unbreakable. My biggest fear, the lightning, had subsided and the weather turned into a steady rain. I sensed the vulnerability of the other riders and relished in it. I began to whistle "Guantanamera," which even irritated Ben and Zeth. "Stop whistling, you freak!" Zeth blurted out, annoyed.

"VENOM!" I replied. "VENOM!"

The Rebel breakaway continued to hammer for the next sixty kilometers through pouring rain, random sunshine, up six percent grades and down harrowing descents. The team, with me leading the way, had opened up a six-minute lead on the peloton. Summit County and Steamboat, gassed and defeated, peeled off the breakaway and retreated back to the peloton, while Vail and Montrose hung on for dear life.

I still felt fresh and wanted to continue the charge, but Ben and Zeth were exhausted and had to slow their pace. The peloton began to gain time on us, and by 85 kilometers into the race, they were only four minutes out, and by the 96-kilometer mark, they were only two minutes behind us.

Coach's plan was working brilliantly. Aspen team riders in the peloton were preparing to reel the breakaway back in, and then finish with some of our strongest guys, most likely Johnny and Stretch, who would still be fresh enough to pull out wins. The breakaway hit 100 kilometers, and Zeth and Ben were gassed. The two pulled off to the side of the road, dismounted their bikes and awaited the SAG vehicle. When Zeth and Ben pulled out, the breakaway slowed even further, and within minutes, the peloton caught us.

"Qué onda—What's up?" I said to Johnny.

"All good! Vail, Steamboat, Montrose ... they all look like zombies. You can pull off now and Coach will pick you up in the SAG vehicle!" exclaimed Johnny.

"How am I going to win if I pull off?" I bantered back.

"You've got balls, vato, but this is my race," replied Johnny as he got up off his saddle and began the final hill climb.

Stretch was on my left rear tire. Johnny was ahead of me on my right, and I decided to fall in just behind them. Telluride and Golden, not known for their sprinters, quickly fell off the final breakaway group and we were all alone—three Rebels leading the breakaway in our first race of the year.

We reached the apex of the final hill, and the road flattened out. A "Finish" banner had been spread across Village Drive leading into Steamboat. Typically, road races drew crowds of hundreds at the finish line, but on this cold, soggy day, only a sprinkling of parents, race organizers and school officials made it out. Johnny looked back to see only me and Stretch to his rear. "Well, boys, who wants it most?" Johnny said.

Before Johnny could even finish his sentence, I shifted to my large ring on the front gearing, drove my right foot towards the center of the earth and pulled my left hand upward towards the heavens, propelling my bike past Johnny's.

"CRAP!" Johnny yelled out, also shifting up to his large gears. Coach Carmouche watched on with utter glee as his

A-Team came careening towards him at the finish line. With head down and mouth open, I threw the bike from side to side, willing myself towards the finish line, but the rigor of leading a breakaway for nearly 100 kilometers was too much. Johnny, making a late charge, coasted through the finish line, with Stretch a close second and me limping into third place. The team gathered near the crew van.

"I thought you would be a little faster with all that water on your back," said Johnny arrogantly.

Coach stepped in, "HEY, HEY, you better be a little more gracious, Johnny. Cruz just rolled out the red carpet for you."

Shivering, dehydrated, and famished, I had no words, but I did have one thing—my first-ever podium finish!

23

FIESTA

"Running would be much better if they invented a little seat to sit on and maybe some kind of platforms for your feet to push."

—Liz Hatch, American cyclist and first member of the Vanderkitten racing team

"School felt a little different that Monday," Manuel said with a smile. "Okay, so maybe it was the third-place medal I was still wearing around my neck."

"You wore the medal to school?" Delatori asked.

"Heck, yeah! Well, to be honest, I wore it under my sweater, so no one could see it, but, YES. I had never won anything in my life and couldn't take it off," Manuel replied. "However, things took a turn for the worse later that day."

As I rounded the corner of the east wing of the school near Summer's locker, I turned to see her embracing Johnny in a long hug. When they finished, she turned back towards her locker and saw me coming down the hallway. I must have had a look of betrayal on my face. She started to jog towards me, but I panicked, abruptly turned around and ran the other way.

"I can't believe this is happening," I thought to myself as I retreated. I was embarrassed, defeated, and completely eviscerated. I had envisioned Summer and I gliding hand and hand down the hallway, eating with one another at lunch time, and kissing in the grassy highlands behind school before bike practices. I went to my locker, ripped my medal off from beneath my sweater, and shoved it behind some books.

I had been working nights as a busboy at a Mexican restaurant in town called La Cantina. La Cantina, known back then for its authentic Mexican food, had been introduced to me by Domi. He had told me that I'd better start earning some dinero to help out with expenses. He also said it would help to show the government I had a job and paid taxes when it came time to file for asylum or citizenship. So, after Aikido on the weekends, I went to work.

I quickly realized that most Hispanics in Aspen had multiple jobs. Fernando Vargas, my coworker at La Cantina, was the perfect example. Fernando worked as a landscaper from 7 a.m.

until noon, then punched in at City Market as a grocery bagger from twelve-thirty until five and finally arrived at La Cantina and worked from five-thirty until close. Fernando's work schedule gave me two keen insights about living as a Mexican immigrant in America: One, I must get into college, so I could develop a career and two, my current schedule, as tired as I was, wasn't all that bad.

Dejected from what I had witnessed with Summer earlier in the day, I wasn't my usual jovial self at work that night. As I was clearing table number six, I paused to stare out the window and gaze at folks as they passed by. To my surprise, I saw Summer walk by with some of her friends. I abruptly turned to avoid being seen, but it was too late.

Summer peeled off from her friends and made a bee-line through the restaurant's front doors. I ducked into the kitchen and retreated to where the bussers organize plates, cups and silverware. To my surprise, Summer followed in right after me.

"Why are you running from me?" asked Summer.

"You can't be in here. This is the kitchen, and I am working!" I barked.

"Well, believe it or not, my dad owns this building. Besides, I happen to be an excellent busser," Summer said as she began to help sort silverware.

"It's not funny. I saw you and Johnny hugging in the hallway. How could you do this to me? I was falling in love with you." I said, as my lower lip quivered.

"You were falling in love with me?" asked Summer.

"Yes," I said as tears began to well in my eyes.

"Listen, Cruz, I was telling Johnny that even though he likes me, my heart is with someone else. My heart is with a very special man; a man of mystery and wisdom, a man filled with strength and power; a man from Mexico," Summer said in a soft, flirtatious tone.

"Wait a minute—I'm from Mexico," I replied.

"Yeah, she's talking about you, bonehead," Fernando exclaimed, as he threw a wet dishrag at my head. I quickly discarded the dish rag, but a small piece of lettuce was apparently stuck to my cheek. Summer drew near and peeled the lettuce off my face, tilted her head to the side, closed her eyes and drifted towards me for a kiss. That's when I knew!

"Knew what?" Delatori chimed in.

"Knew I was in love." Manuel replied.

"All from a kiss?" Delatori questioned.

"That's just it. We didn't even kiss. When she leaned in to kiss me, instead of reciprocating, I placed my head next to hers, pulled her into my embrace and held her like I was never going to let go." Manuel explained.

We heard a loud sigh as my boss walked in. "Hey, lovebirds, can you two at least wait twenty minutes until we close?" asked Felix, La Cantina's manager.

As the staff all but finished breaking down the restaurant, Summer waited near the front for me to get off. Some of the crew had a tradition of playing music after closing. Fernando had a set of bongo drums and was a fairly-accomplished drummer. Big Chef had a booming voice and would often belt out Gypsy King tunes, the other employees would salsa dance from table to table as they finalized place settings for the next day. After being spurred on by Big Chef, Fernando began to pop and tap his drum set in a beautiful Latin rhythm, and Maria, one of the waitresses, brought out a guitar from the back. "Play for us, Cruz." she begged.

Feeling shy and embarrassed in front of Summer, I declined. "Not tonight, Maria. You guys go ahead!"

"You play guitar, Cruz? I LOVE guitar," announced Summer.

Fernando made his hand into a gun and mimicked shooting himself in the head. "Don't blow this, idiot!" I thought to myself, and with a shrug of the shoulders, I said, "Guitar, it is."

Big Chef bellowed, "Guantanamera, Guantanamera ..." Fernando chimed in with a wicked Latin rhythm and Maria began to shake her hips left to right as I proceeded to strum and tap the guitar. I enjoyed guitar and played with a unique style I adopted from my instructor in Mexico. In between strumming, I would rhythmically tap my hand on the body of the guitar. The tapping added a back beat and made the guitar sound full, resonant and percussive.

Big Chef danced towards Summer and reached out his hand towards her. He began to spin and twirl her around as a beaming smile radiated from her face. For a man of 300 pounds, Big Chef had moves more like Enrique Iglesias than an overweight chef. As the song approached its climax, I began to strum in double time, and Fernando was banging on the drums so ferociously that passers-by stopped to watch and listen through the restaurant windows.

Summer and I locked eyes from across the room. In that moment, the earth stopped spinning, time was meaningless and although the future was uncertain, we were forever connected.

24

FAMILY TIES

"I want to ride my bicycle, bicycle, bicycle."

—Freddie Mercury,

lead singer of the iconic rock band, Queen

The next night, I was back working at La Cantina. Even though I was just bussing tables, I truly enjoyed my job at this hot spot Mexican restaurant. Not only did I make great tips and get a free shift meal every night, I began to develop close bonds with the other staff.

As I was clearing table eight, someone came up from behind me and put their hands over my eyes. "Who is that?" I said anxiously. As I turned around, I was greeted by Summer. A warm buzz coursed through my body, and I reached out to hug her.

"I want you to meet my dad, Congressman Campbell," Summer announced.

Apprehension swept through me as I turned stiffly towards the Congressional leader. Mr. Campbell was tall, stoic, and stood with a sense of purpose. His finely-groomed salt and pepper hair, laser-sharp nose and chiseled jawline gave him the look of a Marine lieutenant. For some reason, I pictured him always wearing a suit, but on this night, he wore designer jeans, a sharply-pressed, white-collared shirt and light blue blazer with an American flag pin on the left lapel. Congressman Campbell was already intimidating, but the fact that he disliked Mexicans made me even more skittish. I swiped my hand on my apron in a feeble attempt to wipe my sweaty palms.

"Hello, sir," I said as I extended my arm out to shake his hand.

Mr. Campbell stood still, looking down toward my outstretched hand. It seemed to hang there, filling the immediate space, but somehow also creating a great divide between us. Keeping his hands in his pockets, Mr. Campbell turned towards Summer and asked in a suspicious tone, "Who is this?"

"This is Cruz, the guy I have been telling you about," Summer replied with glee.

There was an awkward silence from both Mr. Campbell and me as we stared at one another. "I better get back to work,"

I said, pulling my hand back as I desperately tried to escape towards the kitchen. I retreated just behind the double doors and leaned my ear towards the dining room.

"What was that all about, Dad?" I could overhear Summer saying to her father.

"You never told me he was a Mexican dishwasher," replied Mr. Campbell in a stern voice. "You said he was intelligent, musically-gifted and a star athlete."

"He is all of those and even more. What does his skin color have to do with anything?" Summer rebutted, clearly annoyed.

"Does he even have papers?" asked Mr. Campbell.

"I CAN'T BELIEVE YOU, DAD!"

At this point, Summer and her father's conversation had the attention of half the restaurant. I stood behind the kitchen doors, partially paralyzed.

"I am sorry, Summer. You are going to meet plenty of guys next year in college; I don't want you to see this kid anymore," ordered Mr. Campbell.

"What?" Summer said in disbelief. "YOU CAN'T CONTROL ME!" she shouted.

"Listen to me, Summer." Mr. Campbell said as he began wielding his power. "Do you still want to attend Oxford next year? Do you still want access to the convertible Saab I purchased for you? Do you still want to go to Greece with your friends on Spring Break?"

"You can't do this," pleaded Summer.

"I CAN, and I WILL," Mr. Campbell answered with steely precision.

"CRUZ IS PERFECT FOR ME!" Summer exclaimed.

I peered through the plexiglass window of the kitchen doors. Visibly crying, Summer got up and stormed out of the restaurant. I wanted so badly to run after her, but I couldn't move. I was terrified of Mr. Campbell. Would he fire Domi if he found out I was his nephew and would he have me deported? For the remainder of the night, I tried to hide in the kitchen, but eventually had to go back out into the restaurant to clear tables fourteen to eighteen.

On his way out of the restaurant, Mr. Campbell noticed me trying to slink back towards the kitchen with a bin full of dishes. He cornered me between the kitchen and main dining area. "Where are you from?"

"Tizayuca," I replied in a timid voice.

"Well, you're in Aspen now, home of the elite, and my daughter is one of the finest girls in this entire town." stated Mr. Campbell.

"I know," I replied. My voice was coarse and shaky as I tried to plead my case, barely able to make eye contact with Mr. Campbell. "That is why I am so fond of your daughter. She is independent, fierce, compassionate and wise beyond her years. I was raised to be respectful towards women, to be attentive to their needs and to follow the word of God. I have the best intentions for your daughter and would never hurt her."

"I know, son, and I am sure you're a nice kid, but Summer is going to Oxford next year and really needs to focus on her grades. Please keep your distance and let her stay on track." Mr. Campbell said definitively.

Speechless and deflated, I slumped back against the wall as Mr. Campbell abruptly turned away and exited the restaurant. I tried to move but was powerless. Maria, who had witnessed the interaction, came over, put her arm around my shoulder and helped me back into the kitchen.

"It's not fair. How can he do this?" I blurted out to Maria, Fernando and Big Chef.

"That's bullshit. That guy can kiss my ass!" exclaimed Fernando.

"You want me to pay him a visit for you?" offered Big Chef in a sadistic voice.

"Boys, boys, calm down," said Maria. "This guy doesn't control the situation, his daughter does. Believe me, give it some time, let things calm down, and hold a place in your heart for Summer. It's all going to work out. It always does." said Maria.

"It doesn't always work out, not for people like us," I thundered back. I grabbed my book bag and slammed the door as I ran out of the restaurant.

I knew where I needed to go. I grabbed the Red Rocket and headed straight to the Aspen Meadows, hoping to catch my mentor and sounding board, Sensei Gold. I had never sprinted that fast through town before. Blowing through red lights and passing cars that were doing thirty miles per hour, I arrived at Sensei's two minutes later. I barged into his office partially out of breath. "Sensei, you must train me harder than ever before. I want to win Nationals at all costs, and I know Aikido will help," I demanded.

"Where is all this coming from?" asked Tom.

"This life sucks. People are jerks, and someone has to pay!" I exclaimed.

"Calm down, calm down. I am not sure what's going on, Cruz, but I will help you. Remember, all great competitors are stronger mentally than they are physically. Meet me at the dojo this Saturday for some special training," Tom replied.

25

EXHALE

"As long as I breathe, I attack."

—Bernard Hinault,
French-born, five-time Tour de France winner

That week, I rode like my hair was on fire. I destroyed my teammates on a training ride Coach Carmouche called the "terrible triad," which took the team east up Independence Pass to the snow gate, back into town and up Ashcroft, back to the roundabout, and up to the Maroon Bells, finally finishing at the high school. The ride was a death march, typically taking three and a half hours or more. Headwinds, late-day sun exposure, and intermittent rain showers wreaked havoc on the rest of the team, but on this day, I finished in a school-record time of 3:05!

After that ride, Coach made me the team captain—much to Johnny's dismay—and was now strategizing how to position me for the team win on every race. That Friday, in the mountainous terrain of Telluride, the Aspen Rebels dominated. I took first, Johnny came in second and an up-and-coming kid from Montrose placed third. I had my long-awaited first-place podium finish. Tom's words from earlier in the week about a competitor's mentality echoed in my head. I was a physically dominant rider, but I knew that to be a true champion, I needed to become a mental giant as well. I eagerly anticipated my weekend training with Sensei. We often focused on sparring strategy, which included employing feints, studying opponents' weaknesses and baiting opponents into traps. I showed up at the Meadows on Saturday morning eager and ready for some serious Aikido training.

"I'm ready to spar, Coach," I belted out as I walked into the dojo.

"Today we are going to do something a little different. Grab your stuff and meet me at my Jeep," ordered Tom.

We jumped into the Jeep and started to head down-valley. "Where are we going?" I asked curiously.

"We are going to get some aggression out and learn how to breathe."

"I already know how to breathe," I replied.

Just then, Tom extended a back-fist strike from across the center console into my abdomen. I doubled over, clutching my stomach with both hands. I looked up, gasping for breath and snarled at Tom, "What was that for?"

Tom repeated, "Like I said, we're going to learn how to breathe."

The car ride down the valley was beautiful and my comfort level with Tom continued to grow. I filled Sensei in on all the drama that had unfolded earlier in the week. I mentioned how distraught I was that Mr. Campbell forbade Summer and I to see one another. I told him how I often laid sleepless in bed, pining after my first love. I told him how I had used my anger and rage to fuel my first-place victory in Telluride.

Tom was an amazing coach and friend. He empathized with me, he validated me, but mainly he just listened and nodded his head in understanding. Tom never told me what to do, but always offered insights that influenced my decisions. He was becoming my best friend in Aspen, and it couldn't have come at a better time.

Thirty minutes later, we arrived at the Basalt shooting range, a favorite hot spot where local hunters calibrate their rifles, practice target shooting and bond with friends. Tom retrieved a case from the back of his Jeep that contained an old Winchester 30-30 rifle.

"Sensei, I may be upset, but I don't want to kill Mr. Campbell," I said jokingly.

"Don't you remember anything?" replied Tom. "To injure an opponent is to injure yourself; to control aggression without inflicting injury is the art of peace. This is the foundation of Aikido," said Tom. "I am not going to teach you how to kill, I am going to teach you how to control your aggression and breathe. This is one of the most important lessons you will have in your life."

I raised both eyebrows. "Fantastic. I'm in."

We found a lane to the far left and Tom began to inspect the rifle. "Life is about balancing the yin and the yang. It's about polar opposites. Darkness is followed by light, evil is washed away by kindness and emptiness is replaced with fulfillment. Similarly, we must learn to balance our sympathetic nervous system response, that feeling of nervousness, excitement and agitation, with our breath. It is our breath which allows us to remain calm and focused in the face of adversity," Tom said.

"Now, listen closely, Cruz. Whenever you're handling a gun you must remember four things. One: always treat the gun as if it is loaded. Two: always keep the safety on. Three: never point the gun at something you aren't prepared to shoot, and Four: always keep your finger OFF the trigger until you are ready to fire." Tom proceeded to show me the proper stance, how to sight the firearm, and how to place the gun against my shoulder.

"You see that target at the end of the range?" asked Tom.

"Yes, sir," I replied.

"I want you to take three shots in a row and try to hit the center of the target on each successive shot," Tom commanded.

I was surprisingly nervous. My only experience with guns had been that horrific night at the border. But my trepidation was matched by curiosity. I wanted to feel the power and control that was exerted on me by Diablo Negro that fatal night in Mexico. I grabbed the rifle; the steel barrel felt cold in my hands and heavier than I thought it would be. I placed it in position on my shoulder; I could feel the kinetic energy stored in its trigger. With hands trembling, I slowly squeezed the trigger.

BANG … BANG … BANG! I let out three rapid fire shots.

"Nice shootin', Tex. You are 0 for 3," Tom blurted out as I looked up to see the target completely intact.

"You see what fear and trepidation can do to you? It's all about the breath." exclaimed Tom. "Put the gun down for a second."

Tom continued, "Place your right index finger on your right nostril, closing it down. Close your mouth and take a long deep inhalation through your left nostril. Before exhaling, place your left index finger on the left nostril and remove your right finger. This is where the challenge comes into play. Keep your mouth closed and try to extend your exhalation out the right nostril for twice as long as the previous inhalation. As you exhale, close your eyes, feel your mind slowing down, and focus on the smooth and consistent sound the air makes as it leaves your body."

I closed my eyes and began to practice.

"I picked this technique up when I traveled to India and studied yoga at an ashram. The alternate nostril breathing technique has a long history in Ayurvedic medicine and is thought to harmonize the two hemispheres of the brain. For me, it has been a great way to slow down and internally focus on training the breath," Tom stated.

A couple minutes passed in silence, with the exception of my breath. Then Tom spoke.

"What are you thinking about?" Sensei asked.

"Nothing, really," I replied with eyes still closed.

"Good, good, that is exactly what we want!" Sensei said excitedly. "Now, follow me. I want you to stand with your feet shoulder-width apart and slightly staggered. Soften at your ankles, knees and hips and gently contract the muscles around your abdomen. Hinge forward at your hips so you can absorb the recoil."

Tom grabbed the rifle and once again placed it in my hands. "This time, don't shoot three in a row. Take your time in between shots with a focus on your breath. This is called interval shooting. After a complete exhalation and during the interval before your next inhalation, that's precisely when you depress the trigger." instructed Tom.

I assumed my stance, placed the gun against my shoulder, and waited for my breath to slow down. After a complete exhalation and before my next breath—BANG! I looked up and witnessed a hole on the upper left corner of the target. I looked over to get Tom's approval. Tom looked back, shrugged his shoulders and curtly said, "Are you going to sit there and admire your work or are you going to take another shot?"

"Oh, yeah, sorry," I exclaimed. Once again, I waited for the interval between breaths. BANG! This time, I hit the upper right side of the target. On my final shot, I prepared the same way as I had for the previous two shots. Determined to hit in the center of the target, I slowed down even further. I adjusted the sight slightly down and to the left from my last shot. This time, I allowed for two full breathing cycles before depressing the trigger. BANG! I looked up to see a hole dead center on the target.

"OSS," said Tom with perfect Japanese inflection.

Understanding that he was giving me the Japanese sign of respect, I replied, “OSS.”

“It has begun,” said Tom.

“What has begun?” I wanted to know.

“The first lesson on your journey to becoming a national champion.”

26

SUMMER IS OVER

"Beyond pain, there is a whole universe of more pain."

—JENS VOIGT, RECORD-HOLDING 5-TIME WINNER OF THE CRITÉRIUM INTERNATIONAL

Summer was terrified of her dad and the power he could wield to make her life miserable. She avoided me at school and seemed to vanish at breaktime and lunch periods. That weekend, the cycling team had a bye. Friday, after practice, I was barreling out of the high school parking lot on the Rocket and almost hit Johnny's Jeep. I looked in the passenger side window and, to my surprise, saw Summer trying to hide under a New York Yankees baseball cap.

"What's going on, Summer?" I demanded as she reluctantly rolled down the window.

"Johnny's family invited me to fly with them to watch a baseball game in New York over the weekend," replied Summer.

"Johnny's family or Johnny?" I demanded.

"Look, man, it's just not your time," blurted Johnny from the driver's seat.

"You don't even like baseball," I said to Summer.

Summer tilted her head down, shielding her eyes from mine with the brim of her cap. "I guess I will see you later," she said.

Johnny put the Jeep into drive and screeched the tires as he blew out of the parking lot. I was devastated. It was one thing to lose Summer to her dad. It was an entirely different feeling to lose her to my archrival on the cycling team and a guy who had terrorized me ever since I arrived in Aspen.

I pedaled my bike to a small, grassy bluff near the back entrance of the school and dropped to my knees. The sun was slowly descending behind Snowmass Mountain to the west and cast a transient glow over the sky. Pink and orange clouds flirted on a canvas of cobalt blue as magic hour settled over Aspen. My senses were acute. I could hear the high-pitched chirping of finches chasing one another through the fall air. I knelt down, placing my hands on the soft, tall mountain grass.

"If there is a God, show yourself to me,
Allow me to believe in lightness again,
Give me strength and courage to continue my path,
And please give me another chance with Summer
She is my light, my love and my life."

At this point, I wasn't even sure why I was praying. God had let my homeland be overrun by drug lords, taken my parents from me, and now, adding insult to injury, had taken away my girl. Were the lessons my parents had taught me about God all a scam? Were the stories told every Wednesday night at Family Faith just fallacies designed to bind me to a hollow religion?

Delatori's voice brought Manuel out of his remembrance and back into the Denver office.

"Do you still have these feelings about religion in your late 40s?" asked Delatori.

"Faith is an interesting thing, Mark. It's something I struggled with for many years. The powerful belief in a benevolent and omnipotent God that was so strong in my youth was stripped away from me that morbid night at the border crossing. It took me a long time to even step into a church again. When I finally did, I viewed many of the teachings and prayers as false hope."

"So, you're not a believer anymore?" interjected Delatori

"I didn't say that," answered Manuel. "I have come to three realizations about religion over the years. The first is that everyone has the right to hold strong beliefs, free of judgement. I value and praise others in their given faiths, and for those who have lost faith; if anyone can understand that, it's me. The second realization is that praying is the same thing as setting one's intention. Whatever someone constantly thinks about, either good or bad, is usually what manifests itself. I believe that praying is simply setting an intention to do good, serve others and actualize one's God-given potential. Whether this is done in large groups at church or by yourself, either way, good things tend to come out of it. The final realization is that, for most, there is an inherent struggle that comes with maintaining one's faith. Many religions talk about 'blind faith,' but it's not blind in my opinion. To me, faith always comes at a cost. The more you give, the more you get. I used to give myself a hard time when I would question my faith as a young adult, but I now know the struggle was part of the process; it has delivered me here."

"Where is here?" inquired Delatori.

"At peace in my beliefs. With all the pain and loss in my life, I have also experienced an abundance of wonder and joy. The people I've met, the lessons I've learned and the abundant beauty that surrounds us is proof to me that there is something greater at

work, something beyond the ordinary, something divine." Manuel replied.

"So, you do still pray and believe?" asked Delatori.

"I do. In fact, I am praying right now that you are still interested in my story," Manuel said with a grin.

"Ha, ha" Delatori chuckled, "Yes, I am still interested, please continue."

I rode home, anxious to see a friendly face.

"A warm bath, some chile rellenos and maybe a game of chess with my uncle should turn things around," I thought to myself. As I pulled around to the storage shed, I saw an old Cadillac parked in front of my uncle's cabin, and I could hear music blaring from inside the house. What the heck was going on in there? I went around the back and entered my room through the sliding glass doors. I ripped Mama's pendant from my neck and threw it in the top dresser drawer. I heard Domi whisper, "Be quiet, be quiet," and rushed out into the kitchen to see what was going on. He was trying to hide a bottle of Jack Daniels by the kitchen sink as I burst in. There was another man there too.

"I'VE HAD ENOUGH HEARTACHE FOR ONE DAY!" I yelled at the top of my lungs, grabbing the bottle from Domi's hand.

"Maybe I should leave," Domi's friend said, and quickly scurried past me, out the front door.

"WHAT IN THE HECK ARE YOU THINKING?" I shrieked.

"Settle down, Cruz, settle down. I'm sorry. I had a rough day."

"You had a rough day? I just saw my dream girl leave with my nemesis, and you had a rough day?" I screamed back at my uncle.

"Cruz, I know you're upset with me, but you have to understand. I, too, lost my girl." Domi's head began to sink towards the floor. His voice started to tremble. "Not only have I lost my wife and child, but I also lost my brother and sister-in law. I feel like a broken man," he said, as he began to weep, and then slumped down onto the kitchen floor.

I sat down next to him and put my arm around his shoulder. Taking a deep breath, I said, "You're right, Domingo. I can't imagine what you are going through. We have both lost so much, it feels paralyzing sometimes. I just know that alcohol is not the solution."

"What is, Cruz? What is the solution?" Domingo gasped, as he continued to sob.

We sat back against the kitchen cabinets; both sighing deeply. "Last week, Sensei Tom ended class by reminding us that it is through adversity that we become great. Maybe we are just building up for something great," I commented. "A while back, you said you would never let anything happen to me and that I am all you have in this world. Well, guess what? You are all I have, too. We have to be there for one other, Uncle," I pleaded, "and I am not going to let anything bad happen to you."

"Your father would be so proud of you, son," Domi said as he leaned against me, resting his head on my shoulder. Domi's breathing began to slow down. He wiped the tears from his eyes and pointed towards the breakfast table, "How 'bout a game of chess?"

"You know, I am getting better, Uncle, and would hate to beat you."

Domi smiled and said, "One day, son, you will be able to kick my ass … but today is not the day."

We sat across from each other, mostly in silence, and played chess into the late hours of the night.

27

TREASURE HUNT

"It is exactly the unattainability, which differentiates a dream from a goal: Goals are reachable when you fight for them. Dreams are not. Athletes shouldn't dream, but set goals for themselves and fight for them."

—Fabian Cancellara, Swiss-born road cyclist, winner of eight individual Tour de France stages

I woke up feeling gutted by the memory of seeing Summer with Johnny. However, if I was going to make a push for Nationals, I had to shift my focus back to weekend training with Tom. The previous week, Tom had told me to pack an overnight bag with warm clothes, a swimsuit, and some basic toiletries for our next training adventure.

I showed up at the Meadows and found Tom loading up his Jeep with camping gear. "Where are we going?" I asked.

"Away," replied Tom. We jumped in the car and headed towards Old Snowmass, taking a right on Capitol Creek Road. The road turned from asphalt, to gravel, to dirt and eventually placed us at a trailhead.

"We're here," stated Tom.

"Where is here?"

"Capitol Peak, one of the most amazing fourteeners in all of Colorado," Tom replied.

"Wait a minute, I think I have heard of that climb. That's one of the hardest fourteeners in Colorado, and doesn't the climb have an infamous 'knife edge'?" asked Delatori.

"Yes, and yes, but I didn't know that at the time. Out of all the fourteeners in Colorado, Capitol is probably the toughest. It is known for having a dramatic vertical relief rising above the Roaring Fork Valley and owes its stately lines to thousands of years of glacial chiseling. It has a long approach, steep grade, numerous talus and scree fields and yes, an infamous knife edge passage that has 'no-fall zone' exposure on either side."

We arrived at the trailhead to Capitol. Tom handed me a frame pack with two sleeping bags, a flashlight, first aid kit, multi-purpose Swiss Army knife, North Face tent, lantern, water filter, Nalgene water canisters, Coleman stove, and various food items, including smoked salmon, steamed broccoli, gorp mix, bananas, power bars and some organic licorice. "Holy cow! How much does this thing weigh?" I asked as I heaved the pack over my shoulders.

"Just under eighty pounds," answered Tom, as he slung a small form-fitting Borealis day pack on his back with an extra flashlight, a couple of small pillows, and a trail map.

"Gee," I exclaimed in a sarcastic tone, "anything else you want me to carry?"

"Oh, thanks for reminding me," Tom replied as he quickly jogged back to his Jeep and pulled out a six-pack of ice-cold Tecate beer. "You can pack these, too."

"At least you have good taste in beer," I groaned.

We began our 6.5-mile journey to the glacial lake at the base of the mountain where we would camp overnight and summit Capitol Peak the following day. Tom, hiking in front, set a blistering pace, and to his surprise, even with an eighty-pound pack on my back, I was right there in his rear-view mirror. Traversing through scrub oak, sage brush and eventually a beautiful aspen grove, we made our way toward the base of

Capitol Peak. After about two miles, the route opened up to an expansive meadow, with views of Mt. Daly and a sprinkling of small boulders.

Tom slowed down so we could walk alongside one another and catch up. "From what you touched on in the Jeep ride down here, it sounds like you have had an interesting week, my friend," he said.

"Interesting?" I asked. "Well, that's a euphemism if I've ever heard one (a word I had learned earlier that week in language arts). It's been a disaster! My girlfriend, the woman of my dreams, left me for a cocky block head, I caught my uncle about to down a fifth of Jack Daniels, and here I am carrying your beer up to a 14,000-foot peak. What did I leave out?" I said.

Tom sighed, "Sounds pretty rough, Cruz."

"I will never get Summer back from that rich, privileged jerk and my uncle continues to struggle with a life of addiction."

"It sounds like you're having a case of an overactive dorsolateral prefrontal cortex," stated Tom.

"A dorso-frontal what?" I replied.

"Your brain." Tom said as he pressed his index finger into my temple. "You see, Cruz, our executive function isn't always so executive."

"Can you speak English?" I muttered back.

"Have you ever heard the Native American story about the two wolves that are inside us all?" Tom asked.

I shook my head side-to-side, "Nope, but you have my interest."

"This story was often told to Cherokee Indian youth as they matured. It goes like this: One evening, an elderly Cherokee Chief told his grandson about a battle that goes on inside us. He said the battle is between two wolves that live inside all people. One wolf is evil. It is filled with anger, envy, jealousy, greed and arrogance. The other wolf is good. It is filled with love, peace, serenity, humility and grace. The grandson thought about this for a minute and responded, 'Well, if the wolves are in battle, which one wins?' The Chief replied, 'The one you feed.'"

You see, Cruz, everything we are, everything we become, starts out in our minds. At the end of the day, your mind is the only thing you can ever truly control," Tom explained.

I was intrigued by this notion of having complete control over my thought process. It sounded like such a simple concept, but I had never really considered it. I gazed up toward Capitol with a sense of restored vitality and the belief that maybe I had more control over things than I had previously thought.

We came to a junction where Capitol Peak Trail intersected Capitol Ditch Trail. The area was flattened with hundreds of downed trees that lay decimated by avalanches from years past.

"Put your game face on, Cruz, and welcome to the first test on our journey." said Tom.

"What's the big deal?" I replied, "It's just a bunch of trees."

Tom, with a skeptical look on his face, stepped aside, ushered me up to the front and opened up his hands as if to say, "Lead the way, chosen one."

I ducked under the first tree which was roughly four feet off the ground. As I tried to progress forward, my pack got caught on one of the branches that protruded downward from the trunk and stopped me in my tracks. I had to drop my hips a foot lower to clear the branch. As soon as I breached the first tree, a second tree was waiting. This tree was closer to the ground and needed to be climbed over. I placed my left foot on the trunk of the tree, which was three feet off the ground, and performed an explosive step-up to jettison myself atop the fallen tree. As I stood on the top of the tree, I quickly realized I now had to jump down with an eighty-pound pack on my shoulders.

At times, I was forced to take my pack off, so I could clear under trees and then heaved my pack over downed trees. This cycle repeated itself for the better part of an hour as we continued to advance through the labyrinth.

"Find your rhythm, Cruz. Don't fight nature, work with it—smooth, steady, methodical, undaunted, that's how a warrior trains."

These words echoed in my head as I hurdled, ducked, dodged and ground my way through the toughest obstacle course imaginable. Eventually the trail re-emerged, and after climbing the final tree in my path, I threw my pack off and placed my hands on my knees gasping for breath. My shirt was ripped, I had gashes and scratches all over my body, and I was sweating profusely. With a slightly defeated look on my face and in a winded tone, I asked Sensei, "How did I do?"

"Sometimes it's simply about survival, and, my friend, you survived." Tom answered.

The sun began to descend in the west, as we continued on the path toward base camp. Once again, Tom slowed down to walk alongside me.

"What is it that you want in your life?" asked Tom.

"I don't know," I replied.

"What do you mean you don't know?" Tom fired back.

"I guess I have never really thought about it."

"Yes, you have. What is it that you want?" demanded Tom.

"Well, I want to be a U.S. citizen, I want Summer as my girlfriend, I want to go to Nationals and win, and I want a sober uncle."

"See? You do know what you want!" exclaimed Tom. "Now, this is the more profound question. How are you going to go about achieving your dreams?" asked Tom.

I pondered his question quietly for some time and couldn't really come up with any tangible solutions. After letting me think on it for a couple of minutes, Tom continued,

"Have you ever heard of an action item list?"

"Can't say I have," I answered.

"An action item list is a list of at least three things that must be completed, in order for one to achieve their goals. For instance, I always had a goal to open up my own dojo. In order to do that, I knew I would first need to train for years, honing my skills. Secondly, I would need to work tirelessly and save money, so once the opportunity arose, I would have capital to invest in the physical space. Finally, I would need to befriend members of the community and build a network of people who would be interested in training with me once the dojo was open. Get the idea, Cruz? Usually, the list breaks the larger goal down into smaller steps, making the process more manageable and seemingly less audacious. As we continue our hike and your mind wanders, begin to build an action item list for each of your goals. What turns the dream into reality is when you write it down. Upon returning from our journey, your homework is to write down your action item list for your top three goals," instructed Tom.

"Got it, Sensei" I replied.

We both looked up towards a huge clearing, "You see how the trees thin out just above that ridge? That's Capitol Lake," stated Tom. "It's also where your next challenge lies."

Excited about the unknown, I increased the pace, and we covered nearly 700 feet of vertical in under twenty minutes. We crested the ridge to an awe-inspiring glacial lake at the base of Capitol Mountain.

On the lake's glassy surface was a carbon-copy reflection of the peak. The image captured the sharp lines, majestic summit and ominous knife edge. Camping areas on the east side of the lake were ripe with field grass, lichen-covered boulders and downed aspen leaves.

"Let's find our spot," Tom suggested.

"Over here," I announced. I pointed to a flat 10' by 10' area that was bookmarked on one end by a rectangular-shaped boulder that looked like it had been tailor-made for sitting, and the other end which had a ridge of tall brush creating a natural wind barrier.

"As I set up the campsite, I want you to begin some 'horse breathing' to prepare for your next challenge," advised Tom.

I looked at him quizzically. "What is horse breathing?"

"Stand with your feet in a sumo squat position." Tom placed his feet two shoulder-widths apart, lowered his hips and lengthened his spine. "Now, move your hands in a circular motion, like you are gathering up oxygen. Breathe in deeply through the nose, while your hands cup oxygen and move it towards the face, then slowly exhale out your mouth as your hands pronate and move back towards the earth," briefed Tom.

I assumed the horse breathing position while Tom grabbed my hands and guided me through the technique. Tom gently kicked my feet into a lower stance. "Close your eyes. Visualize the oxygen coursing through your blood, feeding your organs and muscles. This is your zen, a place of comfort where you build the strength of a lion, the confidence of a bullfighter and the calm of a yogi." asserted Tom.

I continued the horse breathing technique as Tom spent several minutes clearing the camping space of small rocks, assembling the tent and organizing the packs. "Are you ready?" he asked as he completed his preparations.

I remembered from biology class the function of the mitochondria infusing each of my cells with energy. I visualized my heart efficiently pumping blood throughout my arterial system, and envisioned my diaphragm descending in my ribcage and vacuuming air into the lungs. Breathing the air at 12,000 feet felt pure, free, invigorating.

"Are you ready?" repeated Tom, tapping me on the shoulder and snapping me out of my meditative state.

"Yes, sir."

"The purpose of breath control is to increase efficiency and endurance of the system, something imperative for elite level cycling," remarked Tom. "This next exercise is going to test you to see if you can slow your breath down and remain calm while performing a difficult task. I picked this drill up at a Navy Seal in-service I attended in Coronado years ago. It's called The Devil's Treasure Hunt." Tom pulled out a handful of lustrous Native American gold coins measuring two inches in diameter. On one side was an image of a great white buffalo, and on the other was the face of Cochise, fearless Apache warrior chief. "Your job is to retrieve as many coins as possible before you come up for air," asserted Sensei.

"Come up for air?" I asked.

"Yes, this challenge will be performed in Capitol Lake. Don't worry, though, I brought you some protection." Tom said as went to retrieve something out of his daypack. I emitted a sigh of relief, thinking Sensei was going to produce some sort of wet suit to buffer the cold. Just then, Tom turned around wearing a set of swimming goggles, exclaiming, "We don't want you to lose an eyeball at the bottom of the lake. After all, it's only forty-two degrees out there."

The sun had disappeared behind the tall peaks of the Snowmass Wilderness area, and the high alpine breeze had succeeded in whisking away any heat I had left in my body.

"Do we have to do this, Tom? I am a cyclist, not a swimmer." I exclaimed.

"Why are we here, Cruz?" asked Tom.

"We are here to train, so I can win Nationals," I answered.

"Do you believe these challenges will help you on your path?" said Tom.

"Yes, sir," I replied reluctantly.

"Well, put the work in and let's get one step closer to your goal. I have done this challenge with hundreds of students, and the best result has been six coins retrieved on one breath. Let's start out with three and see how you feel."

Tom led me fifty yards west along the water's edge toward an outcropping with a large, oval-shaped boulder. The depth plummeted to ten feet just off the boulder. I was baffled by the transparency of the water and even felt somewhat cocky because I knew I would be able to clearly see the coins as they fell to the bottom.

Sensei tossed three coins in a fan-shaped pattern out from the boulder. "Do you believe?" asked Tom.

"I believe," I responded.

"Well, then make me a believer." Tom said, pointing down to the coins.

I dove in with a strategy to work from left to right, systematically collecting the coins. The second the water enveloped my body, I felt my sympathetic nervous system engage. My heart rate shot through the roof, and adrenaline coursed through my body. I grabbed the first coin and frog-kicked over towards the second, which was slightly obscured behind a rock. When I didn't immediately see the second coin, a sense of panic ensued. I shifted my body 180 degrees back towards the shore to create a different perspective, but still couldn't see the coin. As I swam to my left, I began to move rocks on the bottom of the lake, and soon thereafter unearthed the second coin. I felt the oxygen leaving my body and prepared to retreat towards the shore. As I aimed myself back towards Tom, Cochise's stoic image was staring straight back at me. I dolphin-kicked towards the coin, reached down with my free hand, secured the third coin, and ascended with a desperate fluttering of my legs.

Hitting the surface, I gulped up oxygen in a frenzied manner and flailed my arms trying to get back to the shoreline. "You okay, son?" asked Tom.

I was so cold that I couldn't respond. I simply delivered the coins to the top of the boulder and pulled myself up out of the water.

"I know the water is cold, and I know this is a tough drill, Cruz, but you have to relax, and relaxation starts in the mind. I want you to take three deep breaths through your nose, exhaling out of your mouth, and increasing the time of exhalation on each subsequent breath."

I nodded in agreement.

"Remember your zen, Cruz. You have the strength of a lion, the confidence of a bullfighter and the calm of a yogi," Tom softly asserted as my breathing slowed. "Are you up for another go?" Tom asked.

"Yes, sir."

Tom distributed all six coins in a similar spray pattern. "I liked your strategy of working left to right. This time move with a greater sense of purpose, but don't rush, economize your movements and finish like a champion," stated Tom.

I closed my eyes and took several deep breaths. "Flow like water," I thought to myself, as I dove off the boulder for my second attempt.

Hold Slip

970-306-1890 p

marilyncarroll44@gmail.com

Pitkin County Library C576

CARROLL MARILYN

Wed Sep 23 2020

I quickly found the first two coins and headed for the third. A school of brook trout darted out in front of me, essentially guiding me to the third coin. I watched the fish swim away, fluid, smooth and effortless, a theme I would need to emulate to successfully complete this challenge. I reached the fourth coin and heard a muffled cheer, "Believe, Believe, Believe!" yelled Sensei from above.

The final two coins were on the other side of the boulder. I followed the contours of the bedrock and disappeared from Tom's sight, to the south. I was out of oxygen, my muscles dyskinetic, and my vessels began to vasoconstrict, sending blood inward towards my vital organs. I knew at that point to get the final coins would be an effort coming from my heart, not from my body. "I BELIEVE," I kept repeating in my mind.

I retrieved the final two coins, pushed off the lake floor and thrust my right hand out of the water with all six coins. Sensei enthusiastically bounded up and down, as I swam back towards the boulder. "Why are you so excited, Tom? After all, I only matched the record of six coins," I asked.

"Truth be told, Cruz, the only athletes of mine that have ever tried this challenge did so in the balmy 82-degree water of the Aspen Recreation Center," Sensei reported, laughing triumphantly.

"Gosh darn it," I said, splashing water towards Tom.

As I pulled myself out of the lake into the crisp dusk air, I began to shiver uncontrollably. High altitude temperature swings in the Rockies are legendary. Temperatures often drop eight to twelve degrees in the matter of an hour. This evening was no different. The sun had vanished behind the massive Capitol peak, obscuring any late-day sun, and the relatively balmy fifty-four-degree temperature that accompanied our arrival at base camp quickly became an uncomfortable forty-four degrees. "We need to get you back to camp," stated Sensei urgently. "Your lips are purple." He took off his large flannel shirt and draped it over my shoulders. He then placed his right arm around me and assisted me back towards camp.

"Cruz, you really showed big heart out there. Your progress over the last few weeks is more than impressive, and I want you to know how proud I am of you," he said in a soft, yet authoritative voice. I looked directly into Sensei's eyes, and for a brief moment, could see my father speaking through him.

I was still shivering when we made it back to camp. Tom helped me retrieve sweatpants, a hoodie and ski socks from my pack; then grabbed some wool gloves from his day pack. He then assembled a small Coleman stove and began to heat up water. He handed me a plain paper cup filled with his secret tea, a blend of chamomile and green. I had never been a tea drinker, but when the warm cup was placed in my hands and I took the first sip, I felt like a baby being swaddled. It reminded me of one of my favorite times growing up. On Saturdays, when Mama did laundry, she would remove freshly-dried clothes from the dryer and place them on the laundromat floor for folding. The fresh linens smelled like flowers and felt like crushed velvet, but it was the warmth that attracted me to the pile. For the next five minutes, Mama, half annoyed and half entertained, would plead with me to stop burrowing under the pile of warm laundry.

"Did you hear that?" asked Tom. An eerie symphony of howling echoed through the mountain ridge. Both of us looked at each other with cautious enthusiasm.

"Are those coyotes?" I asked.

"I believe they are," answered Tom. The coyotes sounded off again, and this time it was unmistakable.

"You know, coyote packs are pretty amazing," exclaimed Tom. "They travel together, never leaving a sick or wounded member behind. They hunt in teams, often tricking their prey into an ambush, and they are ferocious fighters, often fighting to the death," Tom said.

"Kinda sounds like the Aspen Rebels Cycling Team: The Aspen Coyotes!" I grinned.

"I like the sound of that," Tom said, then bellowed a wild howl, "AROOO, AR, AR, AROOO…"

I chimed in, "AROOO, AR, AR, AROOO ..." Our howls bounced off the rigid walls of the lake valley echoing into the night. We both began to chuckle. Tom proceeded to open up a beer, which after a long day of throwing my pack around, was in a pressurized state and burst into his face.

Then I heard something that I had never heard out of Tom before, something that I am pretty confident is strictly forbidden by Aikido masters. "Did you just snort?" I asked. Tom responded by cackling, and we both began to laugh hysterically.

In between snickers and yuks, Tom remarked "I hope it's not mating season," at which point piping hot tea exited my nose ending up on Tom's shoes. Tom now had beer on his face and snotty tea on his shoes; we could no longer control our laughter. Gasping for breath in between belly laughs, we experienced a vulnerability and comfort with one another that I had only previously experienced with my parents.

Twilight turned into darkness, and the night skies of the rugged Elk Mountain range unveiled themselves. The stars in the backcountry were unlike anything I had ever seen. Thousands of flickering eyes repeatedly winked at me.

"Speaking of challenges, Cruz, we better get some shut eye, as tomorrow we summit Capitol," declared Sensei.

"Yes, I suppose you're right," I replied. Sensei's words from the Devil's Treasure Hunt echoed in my head, "Do you believe?"

"I BELIEVE, I BELIEVE, I BELIEVE," I thought to myself as I gazed upwards towards the infinite starlit night.

28

POW

"The sprint is tension and intuition, will and desire, self-denial and sacrifice, focus and determination, judgement and vision. For me it was a way to express myself, to show my character, to make my personality stand out."

—Mario Cipollini, retired Italian road cyclist most known for his sprinting ability

The next morning, I woke to a familiar sound: "kee-eeeee-arrr." The hawk that I would see riding up the Maroon Bells often addressed me in a similar fashion. Had the hawk followed me to Capitol?

I unzipped the tent and was greeted by an enthusiastic Sensei. "GOOD MORNING," Tom barked out. "How did you sleep, youngster?"

"Pretty good," I replied. In actuality, I'd had a difficult time falling asleep. I couldn't stop thinking about Summer and Johnny. Were they eating lobster and caviar together? Was he showering her with lavish gifts? Were they kissing like she and I had done at the Punch Bowl?

"It's summit day," Tom mentioned, thankfully bringing me back into focus.

"How long is the hike today?" I asked.

"It's not about length today, it's about explosiveness and power," Tom said.

"Cruz, one of the most overlooked aspects of endurance events is power. Most riders and coaches focus on endurance and stamina, but what do you need when you attempt to pass?" asked Sensei.

"Power, I guess."

"And what do you need when you start a breakaway?"

"Power, I suppose."

"And what do you need when everything is on the line, and you are sprinting towards the finish line?"

"Okay, I get it—power, power, power!" I stated emphatically.

"So, today's lesson is all about power development."

We packed up camp and Tom led me southeast toward the saddle between Mt. Daly and Capitol. After about a quarter-mile of hiking, we found ourselves in a huge field of talus, which pointed us in the direction of K2, a peak named for its resemblance to the second highest peak in the world and situated just before Capitol's deadly knife edge.

"Okay, Cruz, you see these large chunks of talus? I want you to hop upwards from one chunk to the next. Some of the chunks might be loose, so be careful."

"Got it, Sensei," I replied and began to off-load my pack.

"No, no, no, Cruz," Tom replied, "with your pack on!"

It's interesting when you experience a fundamental shift in mindset. The trepidation and fear that I'd experienced prior to the Devil's Treasure Hunt the day before, had been replaced with confidence and belief, not just in myself, but in Sensei. Whatever he believed I could do, I did as well.

"Okay, Sensei," I said dutifully.

I positioned myself in a strong stance with my right leg back and left foot on the leading edge of the talus.

"Remember, Cruz, power is all about speed. Don't hesitate. Turn your power on quickly, just like flipping a light switch," Tom explained.

I thought back to a time in my youth when Mama had brought home a bunch of magazines. In the middle of the stack was an old Batman comic book. I fell in love with Batman. He was intelligent, handsome and most importantly, he was powerful. Batman went around thwarting crime and kicking ass! His "signature" came during the hallmark fight scenes which seemed to happen on every other page. When Batman would down his opponents with a powerful strike, a large bubble caption would appear near the opponent with a word describing the attack, "WHACK," "SMACK," "THWAP."

I proceeded to push off, driving my left foot into the talus. "POW," I thought to myself. I quickly repositioned myself for the next hop, drove off my right foot and thought, "ZAP." I found a rhythm and began to bound from boulder to boulder without stopping.

"CRACK"

"BAM"

"BOOM"

I could hear Tom's voice fading into the distance. "Believe, believe, believe!" he shouted as I bounded up the mountain. Before I knew it, I had worked my way around the west side of K2. Capitol's northeast ridge came into view. The route became more exposed, so I decided to wait for Tom. He soon arrived, and we scrambled along the ridge en route to the knife edge.

The knife edge is what skiers call a "no-fall zone." With 1,000 feet of exposure on either side, the tiniest slip or loss of focus has ended many lives on this section of the route. The edge is so treacherous that many climbers place one leg on either side and "scooch" across the knife's edge as if riding a horse.

"Well, thar she blows, Cruz. The most difficult section of this climb, and your final test." Confidence soaring and machismo pouring out, I stepped in front of Tom and exclaimed, "I will lead."

Tom looked at me and shrugged his shoulders. "I am sorry, Cruz, but you just failed your last test," he explained regrettably.

"Failed? How can I fail? We haven't even started."

"Cruz, part of being a successful athlete and competitor is judgement. Knowing when to go and when to play it safe is critical. I have read about too many accidents on this climb and even lost a friend several years ago. We have accomplished everything we needed to accomplish on this journey. We can sit and admire the summit from here, but there will be no crossing," Sensei explained. I knew he was serious.

We proceeded to sit in silence, side by side on the ridge, and admired the magnificent expanse of the Elk Mountain Range.

29

ON THE ROPES

"My stomach is full of anger and I want to take my revenge..."

—Andy Schleck: winner of the 2010 Tour de France

I returned to school on Monday with a renewed belief in myself and in my development as an elite-level athlete. My feelings about Summer sharply contrasted this newfound confidence.

During language arts, she tried to talk with me, "Cruz, I need to speak with you."

I was too scared to hear what she had to say. I didn't want to hear stories about the fun she and Johnny had on his Learjet, or about how sorry she was things didn't work out between us. I looked out the window and pretended I didn't hear her.

I would use my pain and anguish over Summer as rocket fuel for my races.

The cycling season was flying by. We often raced twice per week and only had the Vail race left prior to Nationals. Since placing third at Steamboat in the opening race of the season, I had not lost.

Johnny and I mostly kept out of each other's way, except for one brief conversation after I won in Montrose. I was standing on the podium in first place, Paul Decker from Montrose was in second and Johnny was in third. From the third-place pedestal, Johnny quipped, "You might be faster than me on a bike, but I got the girl."

To which I replied, "The girl will be gone by next year, but I will have my cycling skills forever." Paul chuckled under his breath. I wasn't pleased about what I said. My father always told me to be humble in victory and defeat, but it sure seemed to shut him up.

By the end of the season, the only rider in the state who posed a threat to me was Paul Decker, from Montrose. Paul had really developed over the season as a climbing specialist. With an outstanding strength-to-weight ratio, legs chiseled from granite, and an iron will, Paul was a formidable adversary. We competed in the mountainous terrain of Summit County and went "toe-to-toe" like prizefighters.

My father used to tell me about an epic boxing match in 1975 between Muhammad Ali and Joe Frazier. Ali had started out fast and even taunted Frazier, but by the third round, Frazier started to catch Ali against the ropes. Although the fight went back and forth, Ali sustained a lot of damage from Frazier pinning him against the ropes all night. It was reported that in the ninth round Ali told his trainer, Angelo Dundee, "This is the closest I have ever been to death."

However, Ali continued to scrap, and finally connected with thunderous right hands in the thirteenth and fourteenth rounds, causing Frazier's corner to throw in the towel prior to the start of the fifteenth. Pops used to say, "Life is like the Ali/Frazier fight—sometimes you're gonna be against the ropes. The challenge is getting off."

Paul and I went at it like Ali/Frazier. He pushed me like no other rider, and was my greatest concern heading into the last race of the season. Coach Carmouche reassured me that based on points, our team was a shoo-in for Nationals, but he desperately wanted to finish the season with a win. I couldn't shake the thought of Paul beating me on the last race, and even had a nightmare about it. Luckily, I knew just where to turn for guidance.

I blew into the dojo that day after cycling practice. "Sensei, I need your help."

"Hello, Cruz. Are you getting excited about Nationals?" asked Tom.

"That's just what I want to speak with you about, Sensei. Nationals are two weeks away, and one of the riders from Montrose is fierce. I can beat him on the flats and sprinting, but he really challenges me on the hills. How can I be a better hill climber and ensure victory?"

"Cruz, I have taught you everything you need to know. Trust in yourself and believe." Tom replied.

"Come on, Sensei. I know you have a trick or two up your sleeve. I am serious, I HAVE TO WIN," I barked.

"Okay, okay, relax. I might have something."

Tom walked me out to the sloped lawn behind the Aspen Meadows. "I have an idea," he said. "This lawn needs to be mowed. Pushing this heavy mower up this steep hill will strengthen your legs, making the hill climbs on your bike feel like nothing." he said.

"Brilliant," I exclaimed. "I knew you would come up with something!"

"There's only one problem. I haven't been able to get the mower started." said Tom.

I grabbed the pull handle and tugged on it, and a puff of dark smoke came out of the engine housing. "No, Cruz, like this." Tom placed his left foot on the blade shroud and his right foot staggered slightly behind and off the machine. "Use your hips, drive through the earth and aggressively pull the handle upwards like this," he instructed.

I found my position and forcibly pulled. Still nothing. Ten pulls, twenty pulls and still nothing. "Any suggestions, Tom?" I inquired fighting for my breath.

"Try switching your hands and feet. I will be back in a minute."

I pulled and pulled and pulled, trying to get the mower started, but was unsuccessful. Tom reappeared several minutes later, "Cruz, it's getting dark, can you come back in a couple days to try again?"

"Absolutely," I replied.

After cycling practice, a couple of days later, I returned with dogged determination. "Hi, Tom, I am feeling confident today."

"Good, Cruz, because that grass is getting overgrown and needs to be cut before the snow starts to fly," replied Tom.

"No worries, Sensei. I've got this." Once again, I yanked the starter handle of the antiquated push mower.

"I will be back shortly," Tom said.

I started with my left hand this time, switching to my right after every ten reps. I would take a short break after twenty pulls and repeat this cycle.

With every pull, I thought of Paul and his hill attacks. His eyes were dark and piercing, like a shark. He had a certain look when he was about to attack. It was the same look Johnny had when he would pass me in the halls at school, a look of dominance. I didn't like this look. It reminded me of the cold, ruthless eyes that peered out from behind the bandanas on that fatal night of the border crossing. "I must sink him." I thought to myself.

With every pull, I thought about winning out the season, placing at Nationals and earning the respect of Congressman Campbell.

With every pull, I thought about winning to honor my parents.

With every pull, I thought about winning to make my uncle proud.

With every pull, I thought about winning to prove to myself I was worthy.

With every pull ...

SNAP! Just like that, the handle cord broke and I toppled backwards, landing on my butt.

"GOSH DARN IT!" I blurted out.

Just then, Tom appeared. "This is a stupid drill. This heap of a mower is never gonna start." I growled, as Tom came around the corner.

"You're right, Cruz. That mower is never going to start," Tom replied.

"What do you mean, it's never going to start?"

"That mower hasn't worked for two years." Tom stated.

"You mean to tell me I have been pull-starting a mower that you knew didn't work, so I could engage in a drill that you knew wasn't going to happen and now I am no closer to winning Nationals?" I yelled back at Tom.

"Cruz, can I ask you a question?" asked Tom.

"WHAT?" I grumbled back.

"When you get off the saddle and are grinding up the hill, what are you doing?"

"What do you mean what am I doing? I am off the saddle, grinding," I snapped back.

"No, I mean, mechanically, what are you doing? What are your arms and legs doing?"

I got up off the ground and imagined the bike beneath me. I imagined driving down with my left foot into the pedal as I pulled up aggressively on the handlebars with my right hand. I slowly looked up at Sensei in epiphany, "I am pull-starting a lawn mower."

"You are pull-starting a lawn mower, Cruz, and now that you have done it hundreds of times, you're pretty darn good with that movement pattern." Tom explained.

I shook my head in amazement and wrapped Sensei, who happened to be grinning smugly, in a bear hug.

"So, what do we do about the grass?" I asked.

"Newsflash, Cruz: No one ever mows grass in early October in Aspen!"

30

PRETTY IN PINK

"Even though I'm a favorite,
I'm gonna just take my big stick and swing it."

—Andy Hampsten,
Only American ever to win the Giro D'Italia (1988)

Surrounded by the White River National Forest and known for having the largest ski mountain in Colorado, Vail wasn't much of a town. It was more of a winter and summer playground. Being one of the world's most affluent small towns, Vail rivaled Aspen in size and stature. However, everybody on the team kept referring to Vail as the "Evil Empire." I never understood what they meant.

"Wait a minute, Manuel, you never saw Star Wars?" asked Delatori.

"Star Wars?" Manuel replied. "It sounds vaguely familiar?"

"Star Wars … produced by George Lucas? Darth Vader and the Galactic 'Evil Empire' threaten to take over the Galaxy? None of this rings a bell?" Delatori was dumbfounded.

"Nope, I never saw it. Out of curiosity, did you ever see The Violin?" reciprocated Manuel.

"The Violin?" Delatori repeated.

"Yes, the Violin, produced by Francisco Vargas. An elderly Mexican musician and his band help supply guerilla fighters by hiding ammunition and other supplies in their instrument cases, none of this rings a bell?" asked Manuel.

"Touché," responded Delatori. "Well, if you get a chance, see "Star Wars." I know you would appreciate it."

"It's now on the top of my list." said Manuel.

We were on the road at 6 a.m. for an early Saturday start time for the last race of the season. The race route was short—only twenty-six miles and 1550' of elevation. The route started at the Frisco Marina, took us through Ten Mile Canyon, past

Copper Mountain Ski Resort, up Vail pass and finished at Vail's base village. At Copper Mountain, the route picked up a paved path that paralleled the heavily-trafficked I-70, but most of the time it disappeared into the White River wilderness, making for a beautiful ride.

"Gents, did you know that it was only 100 years ago that the nomadic Ute Indians would roam the area we are about to race in?" Coach Carmouche said, as we passed through Edwards en route to Vail pass on our bus.

"I have read up on the Ute Indians in Chief Akecheta's class. They were exceptional artists and craftsman, skilled horsemen, proficient growers and fierce warriors," I chimed in.

"Exactly! Prior to battle they were known to paint their faces with tribal symbols representing power and indomitable spirit. So today, boys, I brought face paint," Coach barked out in a gruff voice. The entire team erupted with wild enthusiasm. Coach passed around a silver canister of red paint. "Gents, let's put small horizontal slashes of paint on each upper cheek bone to inspire ourselves, intimidate our foes and channel the spirit of excellence of the Ute warriors." Coach instructed.

The team's 6 a.m. grogginess was replaced by eager excitement as we approached Vail pass, donning cherry-red face paint. However, there was a problem. "This is not good, gents," reported Coach. As we approached the summit of Vail Pass, light snow flurries began to swirl around the van. The snow intensified the higher we went and soon it was sticking to the ground. Snow was not uncommon at this time of year in the high-altitude air of the Rocky Mountains.

In Frisco, Coach made a hard left into a shopping center. “Boys, follow me.”

We unloaded off the bus and followed him into the Frisco Bike and Ski shop. We wound around an assortment of mountain bikes and road bikes working our way towards the back of the store.

“Hey, pal, do you have any ski goggles in yet?” Coach asked the employee, as our band of “Ute warriors” passed the register.

“All we have in the way of ski gear is a bunch of goggles and matching gloves from last year in the bin over there,” the employee remarked. He pointed to a bin full of pink Oakley goggles and matching ski gloves.

“Perfect, we will take all of them” Coach said.

Johnny quickly spoke out, “I’m not wearing stupid pink goggles on the last race of the season.”

“Well, Johnny,” replied coach, “you don’t have to wear them, but when the snow pelts your face on the descent of Vail pass, and it feels like someone is throwing gravel in your eyes, don’t come crying to me.”

In unison, the entire team aggressively reached into the bin claiming their bright pink goggles.

We arrived shortly at the Frisco Marina and lined up to take our starting positions. The snow we had experienced going over the pass had turned to sleet. All the usual suspects were there—Steamboat, Telluride, Summit County, Frisco, Montrose, Golden, and, of course, Vail.

Our Rebel team must have been some sight, rolling into the gates wearing face paint and matching pink goggles and gloves. The team captain from Vail commented, "Look what we have here. It's the 'Pretty in Pink' Rebels." The entire front line began to laugh, including most of us Rebels.

All I knew is that while all the other teams were shivering, I felt cozy, warm and ready to dominate.

"Any final words?" I asked Coach as we lined up at the edge of the starting gate.

"Gentlemen, it is rare that we are simultaneously challenged by worthy adversaries and Mother Nature. This is gonna be ugly, but sometimes ugly makes for the most indelible experiences in our athletic careers. You are not cyclists today. You are Ute Spirit Warriors from the 19th century!" Coach shouted out, as we all cheered.

"Cruz, come here," Coach motioned with his hand and began to whisper in my ear.

"Don't let Paul out of your sight. If he attacks, stay on his rear wheel like white on rice."

"Got it, Coach," I replied.

BANG! The gun sounded, and we were off. The peloton moved slowly through Ten Mile Canyon. The roads were wet and slick as snot. The teams all huddled together trying to stay warm. Team Montrose was to the far left, and I kept Paul in my peripheral vision at all times.

After seven miles, we passed through the base of Copper Mountain Ski Resort. The driving sleet we experienced at lower elevations had once again morphed into snow. The thick snowflakes melted the second they hit our arms and legs, but began to accumulate on our heads, gloves and the road. The pass steepened, and the peloton started to stretch out. Somehow, our team got pinched off towards the back, and I lost sight of Paul.

I wiped a thin layer of snow off my goggles and scanned the peloton for Paul. Just then, I saw movement towards the front of the group. A skinny rear end, wearing a white embroidered "M" for Montrose on the back of his Lycra shorts came off the saddle and made a move. Stuck in the back, I began shouting, "RIGHT, RIGHT," as I tried to get to the right side of the bike path to make a pass. Johnny followed, and we charged up towards the front of the peloton.

The grade jumped from three percent to five percent, which was nothing for me, but as I tried to drive into my crank, I could feel my rear wheel spin. Johnny yelled at me, "Stay smooth, Cruz. Don't crash." As much as Johnny despised me, he knew I was the only chance for us to win Vail and ensure a spot at Nationals.

I shifted to a higher gear, so my rear wheel wouldn't spin, and began to chase Paul down. The grade was now six percent, and the path began to switchback. I had separated from Johnny and the rest of the pack by nearly a minute, but Paul was still ahead of me by about twenty seconds. I continued to accelerate switchback after switchback and could now see Paul.

This was my chance to close. I got up off the saddle, drove through the crank and the rear end of my bike started to slide. I nearly crashed around a hard-right turn, when I heard Sensei's voice in my head. "Cruz, part of being a successful athlete is judgement. Knowing when to go and when to play it safe is critical."

I backed off the gas and decided to "play it safe" and be satisfied to just keep Paul in my field of vision. I knew if I could keep him in eyesight, I would be able to beat him in a sprint at the end of the race. We reached the summit and began the treacherous descent down the west side of Vail pass.

I was surprised how fast I caught Paul on the downhill. Large, fluffy snowflakes continued to swirl in from the south. As I approached his left flank, I noticed Paul holding his hand to the side of his brow, trying to shield the snow from pelting him in his eyes. I blew by him without saying a word.

The goggles worked brilliantly. Occasionally, I had to swipe snow off the front, but I could clearly see every turn of the road. I was even able to avoid a mountain goat sauntering across the path as I came off a hard turn a couple of miles from Vail Village. To my surprise, a large group of rowdy spectators had gathered at the Base Village and were celebrating the first big snowfall of the year.

By the time I rolled into base village, Paul was at least thirty seconds back, with Johnny and the rest of the peloton in tow. I crossed the finish line alone, triumphant, and "Pretty in Pink."

"Hailing from Aspen, Colorado and racing for the Rebels, first place in 'Race for the Summit' goes to MANUEL CRUZ DELGADO ..." the announcer blasted through the microphone. I never got tired of hearing my name called out. Sometimes I thought if they called out loud enough, my parents might be able to hear from heaven.

Coach Carmouche grabbed a handful of snow and threw a lightly-packed snowball at me. Several other spectators followed his lead in a "victory hazing." I jumped off my bike and proceeded to do snow angels on my back. Coach Carmouche ran out and joined me. "What did I tell you, Cruz? Sometimes ugly makes for the most indelible experiences of our athletic careers," Coach said as the crowd hooted, hollered and continued to pelt us with lightly-packed chunks of snow.

31

CRASH

"The only cure for rain dread is to finish feeling you have accomplished something epic ... to feel that you have faced a threat to your very survival and overcome it. The conditions were hard, but you were harder."

—Matt Seaton, acclaimed author and cyclist

"CRUZ, CRUZ, CRUZ," the team chanted as I got on the bus. I received high fives, fist bumps and even a subtle smile from Johnny, as I passed the team to take my seat in the back. Coach Carmouche had picked up a dozen green army blankets that he distributed to the team. We began to peel our soggy, frozen cycling gear off and curl up in the oversized blankets.

The pain wasn't immediate, but as the bus got warm and the heater started to circulate hot air throughout the cabin, everything started to ache. My toes were the worst. It felt like I was standing on hot coals, which didn't make sense to me. How could I be so cold yet experience a burning sensation?

The cold and pain seemed to wash away as I reflected on the last few months. I realized I had gone from living in abject poverty amongst drug lords to becoming one of the top cyclists in Colorado. I went to kiss my mother's cross and forgot I had violently ripped it off after I saw Summer with Johnny. I looked up apologetically towards the heavens, wishing that I could have shared this moment with my parents.

"Hey, Cruz, we are all going to a party tonight at Stretch's house. You need to come," Christian said.

"Yeah, Cruz, we deserve to let loose a little," Stretch added.

"Will Summer be there?" I asked.

They both got quiet. "It doesn't matter, bro. YOU need to be there." Stretch stated.

I told them I would think about it, but I knew I couldn't endure the pain of seeing Summer with Johnny. I arrived home to find a five-foot banner that read, "CAMPEÓN," draped over the front doorway. Domi ran outside as soon as he heard me ride up and greeted me with a massive bear hug.

"Great job, Cruz," he whispered in my ear. Domi had wanted to come to my last race of the season but was immersed in winterizing the Campbell's estate for the upcoming snow season. The banner was his way of saying, "I'm with you, son."

"Don't you want to know how I did before you congratulate me?"

"You finished the season and are a winner in my book, Manny."

"Well, just for your information, I WON!"

Domi screamed out in jubilation.

Excitedly, I began to tell the story. "We raced through sleet and driving snow, but Coach got us all goggles and gloves and I was so patient and then I blew past Paul on the descent and then I won and then Coach and I did snow angels at the finish line and it was so cold my feet were burning which was so weird ... but I WON!"

"Slow down, slow down, Manny, come inside and tell me all about it."

Domi had cooked my favorite, chili rellenos with fresh guacamole and sour cream. We ate, talked, and ate some more. By 10 p.m., I could barely keep my eyes open.

"Chess?" Domingo asked.

"One game, Domi," I replied.

For being so tired, I was amazingly focused during chess. I controlled the center of the board, had my king well-protected and was patient. I couldn't believe Domi brought out his queen so early, forgot to castle, and traded a bishop for a knight. I eventually took his queen, backed his king into a corner and voilá, checkmate. This was the first game I had ever taken from my uncle. Could this day get any better?

"This really is your day, Manny. Don't get too comfortable with your one and ONLY win," Domi said with a wink.

"I love you so much, Domi, but I have to get some sleep," I said as I gave him a big hug and headed back to my room.

That night was peculiar. I was physically and mentally exhausted, but as soon as my head hit the pillow, my mind turned on. I started berating myself for not going to the party. I wondered what Summer was wearing, if she still smelled the same, and if she and Johnny were lovers. My thoughts drifted to the upcoming Nationals, and doubt slowly began to infect me. What if I crash, get sick, or just blow it, and ruin my shot at college?

After an hour of mental gymnastics, I thought to myself, "What would Tom do in this situation?" I remembered the alternate nostril breathing technique he showed me at the shooting range. I blocked off my right nostril and took a deep breath in through my left; then blocked off my left and slowly exhaled through the right. I repeated this cycle on the other side. My heart rate slowed down, my focus narrowed, and as I closed my eyes, I started to calm down.

Just then I heard a "SCREECH, CRASH, SPLASH" which startled me. I vaulted out of bed and looked out the sliding glass door towards the river where the sound came from. A set of car headlights were shining directly at me. My mind tried to make sense of what I was seeing, because I knew there was no road approaching the backside of the cabin.

I realized that someone must had gone off the road near the entrance of the Campbell residence. "DOMINGO, DOMINGO—QUICK! SOMEONE CRASHED!" I screamed. As I sprinted down the hill towards the river, my mental calm was quickly replaced by laser-sharp attention and focus. I approached the scene and saw that a Lotus Esprit Turbo had plowed into the Roaring Fork River. The lights were still shining, yet now pointed downward, illuminating the bottom of the river.

The car was rapidly sinking into the river, and the forceful current of the Roaring Fork was actually shifting the car's position every few seconds. Reacting quickly, I plunged into the water and began pounding on the driver's side window, but the driver was unconscious. I could barely see anything. It was pitch black. I struggled to get my footing on the smooth rock at the river's bottom.

"Cruz, here, use this." I turned to see that Domi had followed me down to the river carrying a large industrial Maglite flashlight.

SMASH! I shattered the driver's window with the Maglite, opened the door from the inside, and pulled the driver out. His clothes were soaked, and his body was limp, making it difficult to lug him towards the shoreline. I was able to pass him off to Domi, but just then the current shifted the car's position again. I knew I would need to hurry.

"HELP! HELP!" came a hysterical scream from the car. I dove down again and forced myself inside the car. It was now halfway full of water and so dark I could barely see the figure struggling in the passenger's seat. I awkwardly grabbed at the passenger, trying to pull her out of the seat. She panicked and began scratching and punching at me. Using an Aikido reversal move, I spun the woman away from me, and trapped her arms from behind in a bear hug. I was able to dig both feet into the center console of the car and violently push off, shooting myself and the woman out the driver's side car door.

Domingo jumped into the water, reached out to grab my arm and snatched the woman away from me. Trying to catch my breath and not swallow any more water, I looked back towards the river and watched as the car disappeared into the darkness of night. I could hear the woman shrieking as my uncle tried to calm her. "Everything is okay, you're safe," he said in a soothing voice. I stumbled on the loose river rock as I made my way back towards the shoreline. The woman had collapsed to the ground, clutching her knees in a fetal position facing away from me. As I got to the edge of the river with utter exhaustion, I fell to my knees next to the woman while Domi hovered over the man and began checking for a pulse. I put my hand gently on her shoulder to help comfort her and as I turned her towards me realized who it was.

I shrieked.

"CRUZ, OH MY GOD, OH MY GOD, OH MY GOD!" Summer repeated as she rocked back and forth, crying hysterically. My eyes shifted towards Domi who was tending to the other crash survivor who began to violently cough up water; sure enough, it was Johnny. "I'm sorry, I'm sorry," he murmured in between visceral groans as he regained consciousness.

32

WALK LIKE AN EGYPTIAN

"Everyone in their life has his own particular way of expressing life's purpose—the lawyer his eloquence, the painter his palette, and the man of letters his pen from which the quick words of his story flow. I have my bicycle."

—Gino Bartali, winner of the 1938 Tour de France and two-time winner of the Giro d'Italia

"Aspen Rebel Cycling Star, Manuel Cruz Delgado, Pulls Congressman Campbell's Daughter from Sinking Car: Teammate, Johnny Roberts, Charged with DUI"

Read the front page of the *Aspen Times* on October 14, 1986.

Upon returning to school on Monday, I had been elevated to Rock Star status. Not only had I won a state title for the Aspen Rebels Cycling Team, but I had saved the lives of two of the most popular kids at school. I received standing ovations at the beginning of every class, got a special visit from the principal commending me for my bravery, and was interviewed by both local papers over lunch.

The highlight of the day, though, was when Summer ran into my arms at the beginning of political science and hugged me in front of the entire class. After the final bell, as I was surrounded by classmates at my locker, Summer was waiting patiently to speak with me. "Do I need to take a number?" she quipped.

"Ha, ha. How are you feeling?" I asked.

"Still a little shaken up, but much better," Summer responded. "I've been wanting to talk to you for some time now, Cruz," she continued. "I need to tell you that ..."

"CRUZ?" A tall, well-dressed man interrupted us, with a camera crew following behind him. "Excuse me, young lady—CRUZ," the man repeated, "I am Ron Zaccaro, from Channel 9 News in Denver. We are doing stories on local athletes who are stars, on and off the competitive landscape. Can we get an interview?"

"I guess so," I replied, as I looked toward Summer apologetically.

"Wow, you really were a STAR," Delatori commented.

"I really was," Manuel nodded. "However, my ego was kept in check by my fear of being ousted as an illegal alien. I was acutely aware of this while being interviewed in front of a huge audience like Channel 9 News. I guess I should have thought of that prior to my fifteen minutes of fame."

I stumbled through the interview, embarrassed and nervous, except for one comment that seemed to get laughs from the audience. Ron stated, "So, let me get this straight; you won a state championship in road cycling, saved a congressman's daughter, and rescued one of the stars of the Aspen cycling team, all in the span of one day?"

"Well, to be honest, I also beat my uncle for the first time in chess that same night." The entire film crew laughed. I wasn't trying to be funny, I had just never beaten him before and thought it was worthy of mention.

"Thanks, Cruz, that was great." commented Ron. "You are a real interesting character. Tell me more about yourself. Where are you from?"

His comment paralyzed me. This was it; my illegal status was going to be unearthed. I couldn't respond. I had no words, and I looked at him, stupefied.

"Cruz, my man!" Someone came up from behind me and gave me a huge hug. Johnny had overheard the conversation. "With all due respect, I need to steal this guy away for a minute," insisted Johnny. "After all, I haven't even thanked him for saving my life."

"Of course," responded Ron.

Johnny grabbed my arm and walked me around the corner. "Hey, man, I know I have been a dick, and you have every reason to hate me, but I really want to thank you for what you did the other night."

"You're right. You are a dick!"

"I guess it's a gift," Johnny replied with his familiar catchphrase and a remorseful smile. He reached out his hand in "bro shake" position.

I returned the shake. "Thanks for bailing me out back there," I said.

"Heck, yeah! They can't send you back to Mexico for at least another week, until we win Nationals," Johnny snorted back in a playful tone. We both laughed and walked side by side out of the school.

That night, I was washing dishes at La Cantina when Maria popped her head into the kitchen. "Cruz, there is someone here to see you," she said. I knew it was Summer. I threw down my rag and blew out through the double doors to the main dining area.

"Where is she?" I asked, turning towards Maria who had followed me out. Maria pointed to a table in the back of the restaurant where a man was sitting with his back towards me.

As I approached the table, I was able to make out his distinguished profile. "Mr. Campbell?" I said with an unsteady voice.

"Manuel, please sit down. I need to speak with you," directed Mr. Campbell.

I slid into the chair and nervously looked at him. He cleared his throat before he began to speak. "I want to personally thank you for saving Summer's life. It was very courageous what you did, and her mother and I are eternally grateful."

"I would do anything for your daughter," I said.

"And she would do anything for you." Mr. Campbell replied.

"I don't know about that," I argued. "She is too infatuated with Johnny to worry about me."

"Actually, you are mistaken, Cruz," he paused for a moment, seeming to gather his thoughts. "Johnny was my idea. I encouraged him to take my daughter to the baseball game to distract her from you. I even asked him to take her to the party the other night that almost got her killed. The truth is that she has been miserable. She locks herself in her room at night and listens to salsa music, sulks around the house during the day and often refuses to do homework. You are all she talks about, Cruz."

I was shocked, and not one hundred percent confident in what I had just heard. A nervous tingle crawled up my spine, and my heart began to beat in a heavy broken rhythm. I fumbled awkwardly for a response "Um ... well ... are you sure ... wait, are you telling me …?" I said, stumbling over my words.

"Cruz, she's in love with you. However, before I allow Summer to see you, I need to know what your intentions are with my daughter. What is your plan?" asked Mr. Campbell

"Well, I want to finish what I started and help the Aspen Rebels win a National title. Then I want to obtain my United States citizenship and represent America as a Junior Olympian. I then plan on being accepted to a prestigious college, so I can continue my studies, and most importantly, I plan on making Summer a large part of my life," I stated with growing confidence and rapid fire delivery. With eyes wide open, Mr. Campbell gazed at me in astonishment. What he didn't know is that when I had returned from Capitol Peak with Sensei a couple of weeks prior, I had carried through with Sensei's directive for me to write an action item list. Not only had I written the list, I rehearsed it every morning while brushing my teeth.

"I can see why Summer is so impressed with you," Mr. Campbell said as he stood up from the table. "Maybe we can have you over for dinner one night," he said as he reached out to shake my hand.

"Really?" I responded, still trying to understand what had just happened.

"Well, not until you bring home a National title, of course," he said, cracking a smile.

As Mr. Campbell left the restaurant, the song "Walk Like An Egyptian" blared from the speakers. I flashed Maria a radiant smile, positioned my arms like Tutankhamun and walked like an Egyptian back towards the kitchen.

33

PREPARATIONS

"To be free and to live a free life,
that is the most beautiful thing there is."

—Miguel Indurain,
five-time consecutive winner of the Tour de France

I packed all my gear, broke down my bike, and was ready for my flight to California to compete in the 1986 Junior National Cycling Championships. This year, we were replicating one of the toughest stages from the Tour de California, the most notable professional bike race in North America.

Coach told us the Tour de California is where the "big dogs" compete, and the route the race organizers had selected supported his claim. The course started out in Placerville, California, and after nearly 100 miles and 8,000 total vertical feet, finished with an uphill sprint into Heavenly Ski Resort in South Lake Tahoe.

"Cruz, you ready, son?" Domingo called out from down the hallway of the cabin.

"Yes, Domi, I just have to make one stop on the way to the airport. I need to see Sensei before I leave."

"Great," Domi said, "I will meet you in the car."

I grabbed my gear, and we pulled away from the cabin in Domi's Jeep. "WAIT!" I screamed as Domi abruptly stopped the Jeep. I ran back into my room, rummaged through my top drawer and retrieved Mama's necklace.

"What was that all about?" asked Domi.

"I believe," I replied.

"You believe what?" Domi asked inquisitively.

"I believe in everything," I replied as I kissed Mama's cross pendant, smiled and looked out the window in eager anticipation for Nationals.

Turning north onto Aspen Meadows Road, we drove under a canopy of magnificent yellow and gold aspen leaves towards the dojo. The aspen leaf changes were in full swing and having grown up in Tizayuca, I had never experienced a fall like this. The shorter days in Aspen meant less sunlight, which diminished the amount of green chlorophyll in the leaves, turning them a brilliant gold. The leaves, gently rustling in the fall breeze, glimmered like gilded coins on our way into the Meadows resort.

"I just need one more pearl of wisdom from the master." I said as I jumped out of the car before Domi could even come to a full stop.

Tom was in his office, drinking tea and reading the *Aspen Times*. "Says here that the Rebels Cycling team, behind their shining star Manuel 'Cruz' Delgado, is poised and ready for Nationals. I am so proud of you, Cruz," Tom said.

"It's all because of the time, energy and wisdom you gave me, Sensei," I offered. "You taught me how to breathe. You taught me how to 'flow like water.' You taught me when to attack and when to be patient. You even taught me how to unsuccessfully pull-start a lawn mower," I said with a smile. "The question is, what are you going to teach me now, ahead of my biggest test to date, Sensei?"

"I am so glad you asked, Cruz. I want to share with you the most profound concept anyone can take into competition—a concept my Sensei shared with me prior to my black belt testing," stated Tom. "What I am about to say is not to be taken lightly. It will alter your entire competitive experience and place you light years ahead of your competition. It will elevate your senses, make jealous your peers and transform your soul."

"Enough already," I interrupted. "What is it?"

"Have fun!" said Tom.

"Have fun? THAT'S IT?" I asked.

"Yes, Cruz, that's it," answered Tom.

I sat down in the chair next to the office door and sighed deeply with disappointment.

"Cruz, this should be the greatest news of your life. Your training is complete. Your work is done. You have proven your warrior spirit. Now it's time to visit unknown places, meet interesting people and do what you love. Have fun and show off a little," Sensei said.

"Was this guy for real?" Delatori questioned. "I wish I could hire him as a life coach."

"I know, he seemed to have the perfect answer for every question. Maybe I will employ him as a speechwriter for my Senate campaign," Manuel said jokingly.

Two hours later, I was on a plane for the first time in my life and was prepared to simply HAVE FUN.

34

IN THE CLUTCH

"When my legs hurt, I say: SHUT UP LEGS!
Do what I tell you to do."

—Jens Voigt,
five-time winner of the Critérium International

"Okay, boys, let's take a look at the course," Coach Carmouche said, as we gathered around a large white board in his hotel suite in Placerville, California. "We start out here in Placerville at the base of the Sierra Nevada foothills. Placerville was actually the center of the 1894 gold rush, and guess what, boys? There's gold in them thar hills!" Coach said, getting into character. "This is the nastiest course you have ever seen. It's essentially one massive climb, 6,000 feet of vertical, straight up to the top of Carson Pass. Then we have a long, drawn out descent en route to one final hill climb at

Daggett Summit before a sprint to the finish in South Lake Tahoe. Is someone going to ask me why there is gold in them thar hills?"

"Why is there gold in them thar hills, Coach?" Stretch humored Coach with an exaggerated drawl.

"Because, boys, we have the most talented hill climber in the nation," Coach said as he pointed at me. "And if we use the hills to our advantage, it's going to translate into gold at the finish line.

"Here's our race strategy for tomorrow. We stay as a team, no matter what. I guarantee there will be early breakaways, but don't chase. Protect Cruz like you would a newborn baby. I don't want any other teams to be able to talk to him, observe him or even spit in his direction. Last year, I raced this course and there is always a stiff headwind as you ride up Carson Pass. If we stay as a team, we can conserve energy by drafting. As long as we keep the breakaways in our sight prior to the Carson Pass ascent, we are in business. This is a long, arduous race, boys, it's all about energy! Conserve, conserve, conserve!

"At the top of Carson Pass, the early breakaway groups are going to be trashed. That's when we attack. The descent down the backside of Carson is long and undulating. If we stay in a tight grouping and continue to work, we will easily catch the breakaway groups by the end of the descent." Coach Carmouche instructed.

"Cruz, at the end of the descent and just as you get to the base of the Daggett climb, that's when we dominate. I want you, Johnny, Stretch and whoever else has fresh legs to drop the hammer. Johnny and Stretch, take turns leading Cruz to the summit of Daggett. On the backside of Daggett, we are in a perfect position for a sprint into Heavenly en route to being crowned as National champions." Coach threw down his dry erase marker like a rap star dropping his mic after a show.

Nobody slept that night, but it didn't matter. We were all eighteen years old and felt like superheroes. The next morning, the Rebels met for a final briefing near the race start.

"Normally, I deliver a 'rah-rah' speech, but today I want you to hear from our real team leader," Coach said as he turned towards me. I was taken aback and sat on my bike seat quietly for a second as I gathered my thoughts.

"When we started the season, we were all focused on individual goals. Through adversity and struggle we have become one, one team with one focus. Now we are like a pack of wild Coyotes. Coyotes are tireless. They protect their own, and they prey on anything in their way. Who can take down a Coyote pack?" There was a long pause and then I yelled, "NO ONE! ARRRRROOOOO, AR, AR, ARRRRROOOOO!"

The entire team joined the call, howling like ravenous Coyotes, and I could feel Sensei smiling from wherever he was. Our competitors had been put on notice.

Riders from California, Nevada, Utah, Idaho, Washington, Oregon, Arizona, Texas, New England and Colorado began to line up at the start. Everybody nervously cased out the other teams, as we sat in position waiting for the start of the race. My heart was beating through my chest, my stomach knotted up and my palms began to sweat. This was IT—the biggest moment in my cycling career!

BANG! The gun sounded, and we were off. The teams moved slowly and awkwardly through Placerville. Each team searched for the best location to reside as the tight pods of steel and rubber plodded down the road.

Immediately after exiting Placerville, the grade jumped to seven percent and things heated up. Three, maybe even four teams, made an aggressive attack. Johnny stretched out his left hand and pushed it down towards the concrete, signaling for the team to stay calm and relaxed.

Just as Coach had warned, a strong headwind came off the mountain as we approached Sly Park Road Summit. We tightened up our formation. Slater, Stretch, Zeth and Kevin were on my front left. Paul, Ben, Christian were on my right, and Johnny was to my rear. Slater and Stretch set a strong pace, but fell back every two minutes, towards the back of our group, at which point the other riders advanced to take a turn leading. I felt like I was doing nothing at the back of the pack, and at the lower altitude of California, my breathing was controlled and effortless.

I wasn't used to this non-aggressive style and could barely see anything but the backsides of the Coyote pack. The ascent seemed to last forever, and although my lungs felt great, there was a slow toxicity building up in my legs. By the time we hit the Kirkwood Summit, my legs felt like someone had put a tourniquet on them and was slowly cinching it down every mile.

"There it is," Johnny yelled out, as he saw a sign for Carson Pass Summit. We needed to close on the leaders.

I got off my saddle. It felt great to finally change position. Johnny and I began to work our way towards the front of our team.

"How's everybody doing?" I asked as I made my way forward in the group.

Kevin shook his head from left to right in disappointment and Zeth looked gray in the face. We had already climbed 6,000 vertical feet and would have another 2,000 to go after summiting Carson Pass. Paul and Ben also looked shot. Surprisingly, Christian, a rider not known for his endurance, looked great.

"What's up with you, man?" I asked Christian.

"Not sure. All I know is that I had a whole plate of Buffalo hot wings last night, and I have been farting my way up the hill." We both laughed.

We reeled in two breakaways en route to the summit and only two remained. One breakaway had already reached the Carson Pass Summit twenty seconds earlier. I said to Johnny, "It's now or never!"

"AROOO, AROOO," Johnny belted out.

As the summiting riders ahead of us sat upright to take shots of water and stretch their backs on the short flat at the top of Carson Pass, Slater, Stretch, Christian, Johnny and I darted towards them. To their surprise, our tight formation ripped by them on the left as they frantically tried to get organized and respond.

We didn't rest on the descent. We took turns leading and shifting positions, racing down the undulating back side of Carson Pass and slowly reeled in the last breakaway. We reached a basin as we crossed into Nevada and could see Daggett Summit in the distance.

By now, we had caught the lead group, which had nine riders in it. I couldn't believe how tired my legs were just from holding an aerodynamic position on the top tube during the descent. The tourniquets were back on.

I didn't recognize any of the lead group, except one guy wearing an "M" on the backside of his shorts. I looked over to see the "shark eyes" staring back at me.

"Hey, Paul. How are you, amigo?" I asked.

"There's no snow this time to bail you out, Cruz," he replied with a defiant stare.

I flashed him a large smile. "GAME ON," I replied.

Daggett Summit is an arduous 2,200 feet of vertical rise, and at this point in the race, it felt like summiting Mt. Everest. Within minutes, Stretch and Slater were gone, Christian was holding on by a thread and five of the other nine riders had disappeared. It felt like someone had poured battery acid into my veins. My legs were screaming at me. All I could think to do was scream back at them. "SHUT UP, LEGS!" I yelled. "SHUT UP!"

We were one mile from the summit. Christian had submitted to the pain along with two other riders. Johnny, Paul, a tall skinny dude from Connecticut and a guy everyone called "Flash," from California, were all that remained. At this point, the only communications between Johnny, myself and the other riders were audible and frequent winces of pain.

I constantly shifted from the off-the-saddle position to the rear-seat position, realizing that even a modicum of comfort was unobtainable. I looked to my left. Johnny was now gone, along with the East Coast rider. It was just me, Paul, and Flash summiting Daggett Pass alone and a good forty-five seconds ahead of the other riders.

The three of us made our way down the backside of Daggett. Depleted, and flush with lactic acid building up in our muscles, none of us completed one pedal revolution on the descent. We bottomed out, entered back across state lines into California and were minutes from the finish at Heavenly.

Paul was the first one to drive force into the cranks after the short descent. Seeing him pedal was incomprehensible. I had to convince my body that I could move again. "SHUT UP, LEGS, AND DO WHAT I TELL YOU TO DO!" I hollered out, commanding my legs to function. My foot pushed down through the pedal, and once again, I had motion.

Five hundred meters out—we turned the corner and I could see the finish line. Paul, who was in the lead, looked back to locate Flash and me and jagged to his left, trying to shake us off his slipstream. We both reacted by lowering our heads, swerving left and following.

Four hundred meters out—Paul swerved back to his right, once again trying to shake us. I heard Sensei's voice, "Slow your breath. Be patient. Flow like water." Flash was glued to Paul's rear wheel, and I was glued to his.

Three hundred meters out—Flash got off his saddle, found his big gear and punched himself forward, out of Paul's slipstream, using a "slingshot pass."

"A slingshot pass? What is that?" asked Delatori.

"The slingshot pass is one of the most effective moves in a sprint finish. It involves the rider in the back using the lead rider's slipstream to help accelerate them into the lead. When done properly, it is like a rock being shot out of a sling. The technique is very effective—unless you go too early." Manuel explained.

Two hundred meters out—the three of us were now in our own lanes. I closed my eyes, rose from my saddle, and found an aggressive position leaning forward on the bike. "Crack, Crack, Crack," I could hear the sound of gunfire in the night sky. I saw my mom lying on her back gazing up towards me, her hand still in mine. People running, yelling, screaming, dying.

"You literally had your eyes closed at the end of this race?" asked Delatori as he scooted forward to the edge of his chair.

"Not only were my eyes closed, it was like an out-of-body experience." Manuel replied.

"Similar to what people report when they die and are brought back to life on a crash cart?" asked Delatori.

"Exactly, it was like watching a movie of my life from above," Manuel explained.

One hundred meters out—I could see the cross high atop the Sierra Gorda range, I switch backed to turn twenty-two. My arms and legs moved frantically, pushing, pulling, driving towards the cross. I opened my eyes and could see my father cheering for me at the finish line, pumping his fist in the air. Summer was next to him, wildly cheering, her hair glowing amber as it caught the late days sunlight of the Tahoe mountains. I could hear a muffled and distorted voice, "BELIEVE, BELIEVE, BELIEVE," projected through semi-clasped hands of Sensei. I saw Domi punching the air like a boxer who had someone against the ropes. Coach Carmouche was screaming towards the heavens, "ARRROOOOO, ARRROOOOO!"

Mama's pendant violently pounded my chest with every crank of the pedals.

Zero meters out—As I crossed the finish line, I looked to my left and back to my right and realized I was alone. My dreamlike state abruptly ended as the roar of the crowd filled the air, and I had the acute realization that I had just become a national champion.

35

DO YOU BELIEVE?

"If you look at cycling as a form of drama or fiction and explore possible scenarios, you will see an ever-evolving masterpiece of human drama up there with the very best – Dante, Homer, Shakespeare, you name it."

—HERMAN CHEVROLET, AUTHOR AND CYCLING ENTHUSIAST

"I had only experienced that level of 'flow' once before in cycling—the time following Mr. Campbell's anti-immigration pep rally, when I blew by the Aspen cycling team," Manuel explained.

"It must be an amazing feeling to find flow and be in the zone. The only time I have experienced a true flow state was after a spring break trip to Puerto Vallarta, and I accidentally drank the water," Delatori said jokingly.

"Hey, man, what are you trying to say about my homeland?" Manuel replied sarcastically.

"I love your homeland, just not the water. So, tell me more about this vision at Nationals, the vision you had when you opened up your eyes with 100 meters left in the race. It was so vivid and detailed, you described it like it was real." said Delatori.

"I described it like it was real, because it was," Manuel replied.

"Was what?" Delatori asked.

"Was real!" he exclaimed.

"How could it be real? Your dad was there?" questioned Delatori.

"Do you remember when I told you about Mr. Campbell confronting me at La Cantina regarding my intentions with Summer?"

"Of course!"

"Well, after that conversation, in true Mr. Campbell fashion, he hired a private detective to investigate everything about me. Although I had won him over, he was so protective of Summer that he decided to investigate me and my family. The detective found a death certificate for my mother, but not one for my father. He flew to Mexico, snooped around and discovered my father was not deceased—he was recovering from a coma in a hospital in Tizayuca.

"WAIT A MINUTE! YOUR DAD'S NOT DEAD?" Delatori exclaimed, as he got up out of his seat with both hands covering his mouth in disbelief.

"Nope, he is alive and well." Manuel said with a glowing smile.

"Well, how the heck did he get to your race?" Delatori questioned as he pulled his chair closer to Manuel's and sat down again.

"Well, apparently after Mr. Campbell unearthed my "hard-luck" story—and taking into consideration that I had saved his daughter's life—he went to Johnny and asked if his family would be willing to fly my family, including Tom and Summer, to Nationals on his private plane. Mr. Roberts, abundantly grateful for what I did for his son, agreed. He first sent the plane to Tizayuca to pick up my dad and a nurse. My father had suffered a traumatic brain injury from the bullet wound which gave him speech aphasia; he had tremendous difficulty reading, writing and speaking and that's why he was never able to contact me. Although Pops was struggling mentally, he had been doing physical therapy every day and getting significantly stronger. When the detective showed him a photo of me, apparently, he sat straight up in his chair and began clapping wildly. The doctors said the only thing that had kept him alive was his intrepid will and his physical conditioning.

After the plane picked up my father, it flew back to Aspen to get the others, including Summer and Sensei. And the rest, as they say, is history."

"That's ASTONISHING, UNBELIEVABLE, EXTRAORDINARY," Delatori said, pausing to let the surprise sink in.

"So, you won Nationals and had your pick of colleges to attend on a cycling scholarship? Where did you go? Cal Poly, Cornell, Dartmouth …"

"Oxford," Manuel said, interrupting Delatori's list of top cycling colleges.

"Oxford? Great school, but there's no cycling team at Oxford!" exclaimed Delatori.

"I know, but there was something better at Oxford," Manuel said.

"What was better than cycling?" Delatori asked.

"Summer!" Manuel exclaimed.

"Wait a minute. You're telling me you gave up a full-ride cycling scholarship and a career in bike racing for a girl?" Delatori said dismissively.

"Mr. Delgado," a voice came through on the speakerphone, "Your lunch appointment is here. Should I send them in?" Martha asked from the reception desk.

"Yes, please," Manuel replied.

"Mark, I didn't give up a cycling career for a girl." Just then the door opened, and Manuel's ten-year-old daughter came barreling in and jumped into his arms. "Mr. Delatori, I would like you to meet my daughter, Brooke."

"Brooke with an 'e'," Manuel's daughter added helpfully, flashing a smile to expose a prominent metal grid of braces.

"I would also like you to meet my wife." Both men turned towards the reception area as a stunning and graceful woman walked through the office doors wearing a beautiful silver cross pendant. "Mr. Delatori, please say hello to my wife, Summer," Manuel said.

"You see, Mark, I didn't give up my cycling career for a girl. I gave up my cycling career for a wife and a family. And by the way, Oxford has an outstanding political science program as well. So, had I taken another route, I probably wouldn't be here talking to a world-famous reporter from the Times. Like Sensei said, it's all about knowing when to go and when to play it safe." Manuel stated.

"Well, now it's no longer about playing it safe. It's about going out there and winning a Senate seat," Mark said, as he reached out to shake Manuel's hand.

As he exited the office, he turned back towards Manuel. "One last thing, Cruz. Do you believe?" he asked.

Manuel pumped his fist in the air and smiled. "I BELIEVE, I BELIEVE, I BELIEVE!"

Made in the USA
Monee, IL
20 August 2020

39022277R00184